FAO-Unesco
Soil map of the world
1 : 5 000 000
Volume VII
South Asia

FAO - Unesco
Soil map of the world

FOOD AND AGRICULTURE ORGANIZATION OF THE UNITED NATIONS

UNITED NATIONS EDUCATIONAL, SCIENTIFIC AND CULTURAL ORGANIZATION

FAO - Unesco

Soil map of the world

1 : 5 000 000

Volume VII
South Asia

Prepared by the Food and Agriculture Organization
of the United Nations

Unesco - Paris 1977

Printed by Tipolitografia F. Failli, Rome
for the Food and Agriculture Organization of the
United Nations
and the United Nations Educational, Scientific and
Cultural Organization

Published in 1977 by the United Nations
Educational, Scientific and Cultural Organization
Place de Fontenoy, 75007 Paris

© FAO/Unesco 1977
Printed in Italy

ISBN 92-3-101344-0

The project for a joint FAO/Unesco Soil Map of the World was undertaken following a recommendation of the International Society of Soil Science. It is the first attempt to prepare, on the basis of international cooperation, a soil map covering all the continents of the world in a uniform legend, thus enabling the correlation of soil units and comparisons on a global scale. The project, which started in 1961, fills a gap in present knowledge of soil potentialities throughout the world and provides a useful instrument in planning agricultural and economic development programmes.

The project has been carried out under the scientific authority of an international advisory panel, within the framework of FAO and Unesco programmes. The different stages of the work included comparative studies of soil maps, field and laboratory work, and the organization of international expert meetings and study tours. The secretariat of the joint project, located at FAO Headquarters, was vested with the responsibility of compiling the technical information, correlating the studies and drafting the maps and text. FAO and Unesco shared the expenses involved in the realization of the project, and Unesco undertook publication of its results. The services of an associate expert were made available by the Government of the Netherlands to assist in the preparation of the Soil Map of South Asia.

The present volume, covering the soils of South Asia, is the seventh of a set of ten which make up the complete publication of the Soil Map of the World. The first volume records introductory information and presents the definitions of the elements of the legend which is used uniformly throughout the publication. Each of the nine following volumes comprises an explanatory text and the corresponding map sheets covering the main regions of the world.

FAO and Unesco wish to express their gratitude to the government institutions, the International Society of Soil Science, and the many individual soil scientists who have contributed so much to this international project.

CONTENTS

This volume describes the South Asian section of the 1:5 000 000 Soil Map of the World.

The maps

The two map sheets which make up the Soil Map of South Asia are drawn on topographic base maps of the 1:5 000 000 series of the American Geographical Society. The map units are associations of soil units divided into texture and slope classes. They are marked on the maps by symbols. The dominant soils are shown by colours while phase differences are shown by overprints.

A small inset map shows three grades of reliability of the soil information from which the map was compiled.

Detailed definitions of the soil units and full descriptions of all the terms used may be found in Volume I of the set.

The text

The first chapter describes the development of the project in South Asia and gives some notes on uses of the map. The second acknowledges the cooperation of the agencies and the many persons who contributed to the maps and text, and the third gives a summary of the material in Volume I on the map units, legend and sources of information.

The main chapters of this volume deal with environmental conditions, soil distribution and land use.

ENVIRONMENTAL CONDITIONS

Chapter 4 contains brief accounts of the four environmental factors which influence the development and use of soils: climate, vegetation, geomorphology and geology and lithology.

Climate is discussed on the basis of eight broad climatic regions. Since the criteria used in delimiting units are those that are important to crop growth, the climatic map is supplementary to the soil map in the transfer of crop information from one part of the world to another. Here only the higher categories are discussed. The main climatic regions are outlined on a small-scale map (Figure 1).

Vegetation is discussed on the basis of 14 broad vegetation regions which are subdivided into 34 subregions and distinguished according to habitat (either climatic or edaphic) and the physiognomy and structure of the vegetation. The distribution of the vegetation regions is outlined on a small-scale map (Figure 2). The text gives some brief notes on each region and on the location and nature of its subregions.

Geomorphology and landscape development are then treated in terms of three main groups of morphostructural regions: the Indian shield and the Indo-Gangetic plain, the Arabian shield and the associated Median zone, and the Tethys geosyncline. A small-scale map (Figure 3) shows the geomorphological subregions.

Geology is considered under the three regions mentioned above, and *lithology* under 10 regions. There are two small-scale maps (Figures 4 and 5), one of geological regions, which are considered region by region in the text, and the other of lithological regions. The text outlines the geological origins and nature of the main surfaces at present exposed.

SOILS AND LAND USE

Chapters 5 and 6, describing the soils of the subcontinent, contain an extensive table of soil associations, an account of the distribution of the main soils, and a discussion of land use and soil suitabilities for agriculture.

The table of *soil associations* lists all the map units in alphabetical order of symbols. Other columns show:

Associated soils
Inclusions
Phases
Areas of units in 1 000 hectares
Climate symbols
Countries of occurrence

The *distribution of major soils* is discussed on the basis of 19 broad soil regions, which are outlined on a small-scale map (Figure 6). The main soils of each region are discussed in relation to factors of the environment.

Present land use and suitabilities for agriculture are discussed at first in general. Then the main soils are considered separately, their present use being described and the suitability of the land outlined.

The cultivated land is managed generally in small units by traditional methods, yielding only slightly over subsistence. Substantial increases in agricultural production are therefore possible by making better use of soils.

CONCLUSIONS

A general outline of the distribution of main soil units and their land use is given at the end of Chapter 6. Arid soils with rough grazing and shallow mountain soils cover about 60% of South Asia. Soils considered as suitable for agriculture where topography is not a limiting factor cover some 40% of the area.

The Appendix

Site and profile data, including profile descriptions and analyses, are given in the Appendix for some of the main soil units. For easier reference, the soil profiles are listed in alphabetical order of symbols.

Le présent volume décrit la partie relative à l'Asie du Sud de la Carte mondiale des sols au 1 : 5 000 000.

Les cartes

Les deux feuilles qui constituent la carte des sols de l'Asie du Sud ont été établies d'après le fond topographique au 1 : 5 000 000 des cartes de l'American Geographical Society. Les unités cartographiques sont des associations d'unités pédologiques auxquelles on a attribué les classes de texture et de pente du sol dominantes. Elles sont indiquées sur la carte par des symboles (lettres et chiffres). Les sols dominants sont représentés par des couleurs, tandis que les différentes phases sont indiquées en surcharge.

Une carte à petite échelle figurant en cartouche sur la carte principale précise les trois degrés de fiabilité des renseignements pédologiques à partir desquels la carte a été établie.

On trouvera dans le volume I de cette série les définitions détaillées des unités pédologiques et les descriptions complètes de tous les termes utilisés.

Le texte

Le premier chapitre fait l'historique du projet pour l'Asie du Sud et donne quelques informations sur l'utilisation des cartes. Le deuxième chapitre rend hommage aux institutions et à tous ceux qui ont contribué à l'établissement des cartes et du texte. Le troisième donne un résumé du contenu du volume I en ce qui concerne les unités cartographiques, la légende et les sources d'informations.

Les chapitres suivants traitent du milieu, de la répartition des sols et de leur utilisation.

Le milieu

Le chapitre 4 rend compte brièvement des quatre facteurs du milieu dont dépend la répartition des sols: climat, végétation, géomorphologie, géologie et lithologie.

Le *climat* est traité sur la base de huit grandes régions climatiques. Etant donné qu'on a utilisé comme critères pour la détermination des unités pédologiques, ceux qui sont importants pour la croissance des plantes, la carte des climats complète la carte des sols pour le transfert des renseignements sur les cultures, d'une partie du monde à l'autre. On n'a examiné ici que les grandes catégories. Les principales régions climatiques sont représentées sur une carte à petite échelle (figure 1).

La *végétation* est examinée sur la base de 14 grandes régions végétales, qui sont subdivisées en 34 sous-régions et classées en fonction de l'habitat (climatique ou édaphique), de la physionomie et de la structure de la végétation. La répartition des régions végétales est représentée sur une carte à petite échelle (figure 2). On trouvera dans le texte de brèves indications sur chaque région et sur la localisation et la nature de ses sous-régions.

La *géomorphologie* et le développement du paysage sont ensuite traités dans le cadre de trois grands groupes morphostructurels de régions: le bouclier indien et la plaine indo-gangétique, le bouclier arabe et la zone médiane associée, et le géosynclinal de la Téthys. Une carte à petite échelle montre les sous-régions géomorphologiques (figure 3).

La *géologie* est examinée dans le cadre des trois régions susmentionnées et la *lithologie* dans le cadre de dix régions. Deux cartes à petite échelle sont incluses (figures 4 et 5), l'une pour les régions géologiques, qui sont traitées par région dans le texte, et l'autre pour les régions lithologiques. Le texte donne des indications sur les origines géologiques et la nature des principales formations affleurant actuellement en surface.

Les sols et leurs utilisations

Les chapitres 5 et 6, dans lesquels sont décrits les sols du sous-continent sud-asiatique, contiennent un tableau détaillé des associations pédologiques qu'on y rencontre, une description de la répartition des principaux sols, et un examen de leur utilisation et de leur vocation agricole.

Le tableau des associations pédologiques énumère toutes les unités cartographiques dans l'ordre alphabétique des symboles. Les autres colonnes sont consacrées aux rubriques suivantes:

Sols associés

Inclusions

Phases

Superficie des unités en milliers d'hectares

Symboles climatiques

Répartition par pays

La répartition des principaux sols est faite suivant 19 grandes régions pédologiques, représentées sur une carte à petite échelle (figure 6). Les principaux sols de chacune de ces régions sont examinés en fonction des facteurs du milieu.

L'utilisation actuelle des terres et leur vocation agricole sont d'abord examinées d'un point de vue général; les principaux types de sols sont ensuite étudiés séparément; il est donné une description de leur utilisation actuelle, ainsi que des indications sur leur vocation agricole.

Les terres actuellement cultivées sont le plus souvent constituées de petites parcelles traitées selon des méthodes traditionnelles, et les rendements ne dépassent guère ceux d'une économie de subsistance. Il est donc possible d'augmenter sensiblement la production agricole en tirant un meilleur parti des sols.

CONCLUSIONS

Des indications générales sur la répartition des principales unités pédologiques et l'utilisation de leurs terres sont données à la fin du chapitre 6. Les sols arides à pâturages grossiers et sols montagneux peu profonds couvrent environ 60 pour cent de la surface de l'Asie du Sud. Les sols jugés aptes à l'agriculture, dans les zones où la topographie n'est pas un facteur limitatif, occupent environ 40 pour cent de cette surface.

Annexe

On trouvera dans l'annexe des données sur les stations et les profils, ainsi que des descriptions et analyses de profils de certaines des principales unités pédologiques. Pour plus de facilité, la liste des profils pédologiques est donnée dans l'ordre alphabétique des symboles.

В этом томе описывается южноазиатский участок почвенной карты мира в масштабе 1:5 000 000.

Карты

Почвенная карта Южной Азии, состоящая из двух листов, составлена на основе топографических карт серии 1:5 000 000 Американского географического общества. Картографические единицы представляют собой совокупности почвенных единиц, подразделенные на классы по текстуре и склонам. Они отмечены на картах условными знаками. Преобладающие почвы показаны в цвете, а разность фаз показана штриховкой.

Небольшая карта-врезка показывает три степени достоверности информации о почвах, на основе которой была составлена карта.

Подробные определения почвенных единиц и полное описание всех применяемых терминов нахоядтся в томе I комплекта.

Текст

В первой главе описывается развитие проекта в Южной Азии и излагаются некоторые замечания по использованию карты. Во второй главе высказывается признательность за сотрудничество учреждениям и большому числу лиц, которые содействовали подготовке карт и текста. В третьей главе излагается резюме материала тома I по картографическим единицам, легенде и источникам информации.

В основных главах этого тома рассматриваются условия окружающей среды, распределение почв и землепользование.

УСЛОВИЯ ОКРУЖАЮЩЕЙ СРЕДЫ

В главе 4 содержится краткое описание четырех факторов окружающей среды, которые оказывают влияние на развитие и использование почв: климат, растительность, геоморфология и геология и литология.

Климат рассматривается на основе восьми обширных климатических районов. Ввиду того, что критерии, используемые для определения единиц, являются такими критериями, которые важны для возделывания сельскохозяйственных культур, климатическая карта дополняет почвенную карту при передаче информации об урожаях из одной части мира в другую. В данном случае рассматриваются лишь высшие категории. Основные климатические районы показаны на мелкомасштабной карте (Фиг. 1).

Растительность рассматривается на основе 14 обширных районов растительности, которые подразделяются на 34 подрайонов и различаются по ареалам (климатическим или почвенным) и физиогномике и расительной структуре. Распределение районов растительности показано на мелкомасштабной карте (Фиг. 2). В тексте кратко говорится о каждом районе, а также о размещении и характере его подрайонов.

Геоморфология и развитие ландшафта рассматриваются с точки зрения трех основных групп морфоструктурных районов: Индийской платформы, Индо-Гангской равнины, Аравийской платформы и сопредельной Срединной зоны, а также геосинклинали Тетиса. На мелкомасштабной карте показаны геоморфологические подрайоны (Фиг. 3).

Геология рассматривается в рамках трех упомянутых выше районов, а литология - в рамках десяти районов. В том включены две мелкомасштабные карты (Фиг. 4 и 5); карта геологических районов, которые рассматриваются порайонно в тексте, и литологическая карта. В тексте описывается геологическое происхождение и характер основных обнаженных в настоящее время поверхностей.

Использование почв и земель - В главах 5 и 6 описываются почвы подконтинента, а также содержится обширная таблица почвенных ассоциаций, перечень распределения основных почв и рассматриваются проблемы землепользования и пригодности почв для сельского хозяйства.

В таблице почвенных ассоциаций перечисляются все картографические единицы в алфавитном порядке условных знаков. В других колонках приводятся:

　　ассоциированные почвы
　　включения
　　фазы
　　площади единиц в 1 000 га
　　климатические условные обозначения
　　страны распространения

Распространение основных почв рассматривается на основе 19 обширных почвенных районов, показанных на мелкомасштабной карте (Фиг.6). Основные почвы каждого района рассматриваются в связи с факторами окружающей среды.

Нынешнее землепользование и пригодность земель для ведения сельского хозяйства рассматривается сначала в общем плане.Затем основные почвы рассматриваются отдельно, описывается их использование в настоящее время и пригодность упомянутых земель.

Культивированное землепользование осуще-

ствляется как правило на небольших площадях традиционными методами, что позволяет получать урожай лишь несколько больше необходимого для пропитания. В связи с этим возможен значительный подъем сельскохозяйственного производства за счет лучшего использования почв.

Выводы

В конце главы 6 дается общая картина распределения основных почвенных единиц и использования их земли. Аридные почвы с грубым выпасом и маломощные горные почвы покрывают около 60 процентов территории Южной Азии.Почвы рассматриваются в качестве пригодных для сельского хозяйства там, где не являющийся сдерживающим фактором рельеф покрывает около 40 проц.территории.

Приложение

По некоторым основным почвенным единицам в Приложении приводятся данные о местах распространения и профилях, включая описание профилей и анализы.Для более удобного пользования почвенные профили приводятся в алфавитном порядке условных знаков.

En este volumen se describe la sección de Asia meridional del Mapa Mundial de Suelos a escala 1 : 5 000 000.

Los mapas

Las dos hojas con mapas que comprenden el mapa de suelos de Asia meridional se han trazado sobre la base de los mapas topográficos de la serie a escala 1 : 5 000 000 de la American Geographical Society. Las unidades del mapa son asociaciones de unidades de suelos divididas en clases texturales y de inclinación. Se indican en el mapa por medio de símbolos. Los suelos dominantes se muestran por colores, mientras que las diferentes fases se indican con sobreimpresiones.

Un pequeño mapa intercalado en un recuadro indica tres grados de fiabilidad de la información sobre suelos que sirvió de base para la compilación del mapa.

En el Volumen I de la serie pueden encontrarse definiciones detalladas de las unidades de suelos y descripciones completas de todos los términos utilizados.

El texto

En el primer capítulo se describe el desarrollo del proyecto en Asia meridional y se dan unas notas sobre los usos posibles del mapa. En el segundo se da cuenta de la cooperación de organismos y las muchas personas que han colaborado en los mapas y en el texto, y en el tercero se presenta un resumen del material contenido en el Volumen I sobre las unidades cartográficas, la leyenda y las fuentes de información.

Los principales capítulos de este volumen tratan de las condiciones ambientales, distribución de los suelos y aptitud de las tierras.

CONDICIONES DEL MEDIO

El Capítulo 4 contiene breves reseñas de los cuatro factores del medio que influyen sobre el desarrollo y utilización de los suelos: clima, vegetación, geomorfología y geología y litología.

El *clima* se estudia sobre la base de ocho amplias regiones climáticas. Dado que los criterios adoptados para delimitar las unidades son aquellos que interesan al crecimiento de las plantas, el mapa climático sirve así de complemento al mapa de suelos para la transferencia de información sobre cultivos de una parte del mundo a otra. Aquí se examinan únicamente las categorías superiores. Las principales regiones climáticas se bosquejan en un mapa a pequeña escala (Figura 1).

La *vegetación* se estudia sobre la base de 14 amplias regiones de vegetación subdivididas en 34 subregiones y diferenciadas según el habitat (ya sea climático o edáfico) y la fisionomía y estructura de la vegetación. La distribución de las regiones de vegetación se bosqueja en un mapa a pequeña escala (Figura 2). El texto contiene algunas breves notas sobre cada región y sobre la ubicación y naturaleza de las subregiones.

La *geomorfología* y el desarrollo del paisaje se tratan en función de tres grupos principales de regiones morfoestructurales: la plataforma india y la planicie del Indo-Ganges, la plataforma árabe con la zona mediana asociada y la zona del Tetis. Un mapa a pequeña escala muestra las subregiones geomorfológicas (Figura 3).

La *geología* se estudia para las tres regiones mencionadas anteriormente, y la *litología* para diez. Existen dos mapas a pequeña escala (figuras 4 y 5), uno de regiones geológicas, que se examinan región por región en el texto, y el otro de regiones litológicas. El texto esboza los orígenes geológicos y la naturaleza de las principales superficies expuestas al presente.

LOS SUELOS Y EL USO DE LA TIERRA

Los capítulos 5 y 6, que describen los suelos del subcontinente, contienen un extenso cuadro de las asociaciones, una reseña de la distribución de los suelos principales y un estudio sobre el uso de la tierra y la aptitud de los suelos para la agricultura.

En el cuadro de asociaciones de suelos se enumeran todas las unidades del mapa por orden alfabético de los símbolos. En otras columnas se presentan: suelos asociados, inclusiones, fases, superficie de las unidades en miles de ha, símbolos climáticos, países en que se presentan.

La distribución de los suelos principales se examina sobre la base de 16 grandes regiones de suelos que se delinean en un mapa a pequeña escala (Figura 6). Los suelos principales de cada región se estudian en relación con los factores del ambiente.

El uso actual de la tierra y su aptitud para la agricultura se examinan en primer lugar en líneas generales. Después se estudian los suelos principales por separado describiéndose su utilización actual y bosquejándose la aptitud de las tierras.

Las tierras cultivadas se explotan generalmente en pequeñas unidades mediante métodos tradicionales y dan rendimientos sólo ligeramente superiores a los de subsistencia. Por consiguiente, son posibles incrementos notables en la producción agrícola haciendo un mejor uso de los suelos.

CONCLUSIONES

Al final de Capítulo 6 se da un bosquejo general de la distribución de las unidades de suelos principales y de la utilización de las tierras. Los suelos áridos con pastos groseros y los suelos montañosos someros cubren alrededor del 60 por ciento del Asia meridional. Los suelos considerados como aptos para la agricultura cuando la topografía no constituye un factor limitador abarcan el 40 por ciento restante.

Apéndice

En el Apéndice se dan datos sobre emplazamiento y perfiles, incluso descripciones y análisis de perfiles para algunas de las principales unidades de suelos. Para facilitar la consulta los perfiles de suelos se enumeran en el orden alfabético de los símbolos.

1. INTRODUCTION

History of the project [1]

Recognizing the need for an integrated knowledge of the soils of the world, the Seventh Congress of the International Society of Soil Science held in 1960 in Madison, Wisconsin, United States, recommended that ways and means be found for the publication of soil maps of the great regions of the world. As a follow-up to this recommendation, FAO and Unesco agreed in 1961 to prepare jointly a Soil Map of the World based on the compilation of available soil survey material and on additional field correlation. The secretariat of the joint project was located at FAO Headquarters in Rome. It was responsible for collecting and compiling the technical information, undertook correlation studies, and drafted the maps and text.

In June 1961 an Advisory Panel composed of prominent soil scientists representing various parts of the world was convened by FAO and Unesco to study the methodological, scientific, and various other problems related to the preparation of a Soil Map of the World.[2]

A Near East Regional Meeting on Soil Classification and Survey had already been convened by FAO in December 1959 in Beirut at the invitation of the Government of Lebanon. The main purposes of the meeting were to promote soil survey programmes and to standardize soil investigation and classification methods with a view to preparing a map of the soil resources of the region.

In accordance with the Advisory Panel's recommendation concerning organization of regional correlation, a Soil Correlation Seminar for South and Central Asia took place in Tashkent, Uzbekistan, U.S.S.R., in September 1962. A soil map of Asia at 1 : 6 000 000 scale by V. Kovda and E. Lobova was presented at the Seminar. Draft soil maps of Afghanistan, Burma, Sri Lanka, India and Iran were also presented. The Seminar was followed by a study tour which provided an opportunity for correlating representative soil units in the region.

A first draft of a general soil map of the Near East, based on information made available at the Seminar, was prepared in FAO and presented in 1964 at the Eighth Congress of the International Society of Soil Science held in Bucharest, Romania.

A draft soil map of India at 1 : 3 000 000 scale was prepared by the All India Soil and Land Use Survey and presented at a Soil Correlation and Appraisal Meeting held in New Delhi in April 1965. Correlation of the main units of the map with international classification schemes and soil maps of neighbouring countries such as Pakistan, Nepal and Sri Lanka was a main concern of the meeting and related study tour.

In 1967, the All India Soil and Land Use Survey kindly arranged for an extended field correlation trip by two FAO consultants. As a result, a first draft of a soil map of India, based on the newly established FAO soil units, was completed in time for presentation at the Ninth Congress of the International Society of Soil Science, held in Adelaide, Australia, in 1968.

The final draft of the general Soil Map of South Asia was compiled in the Soil Resources Development and Conservation Service of FAO in 1972. It incorporates updated information on soil distribution resulting from a number of FAO/UNDP field projects, and entirely revised soil maps for several countries such as Bangladesh, Iran, Iraq, Israel and Pakistan.

The main sources of information used in the preparation of the Soil Map of South Asia are described in Chapter 3.

---

[1] The history of the project as a whole is dealt with more completely in Volume I.

[2] The participants in this meeting were:
  Consultants: G. Aubert (France), M. Camargo (Brazil), J. D'Hoore (Belgium), Mrs. E. Lobova (U.S.S.R.), S.P. Raychaudhuri (India), G.D. Smith (United States), C.G. Stephens (Australia), R. Tavernier (Belgium), H. Taylor (New Zealand), I.V. Tiurin (U.S.S.R.), F.A. van Baren (Netherlands).
  Unesco Secretariat: V. Kovda and M. Batisse.
  FAO Secretariat: D. Luis Bramão, R. Dudal and F. George.

Objectives

Transfer of knowledge and experience from one area of the earth to another can only be successful when allowance is made for similarities and differences in the geographical, soil and climatic conditions of the regions or countries involved. Furthermore, the economic feasibility of different management techniques under prevailing socio-economic conditions needs to be assessed before they can be recommended for adoption. In order to do so, reliable information on the nature and distribution of the major soils of the world is of fundamental importance. However, the preparation of regional and continental soil maps requires a uniform legend and nomenclature and the correlation of existing soil classification systems. One of the principal objectives of the FAO/Unesco Soil Map of the World project was to promote cooperation among soil scientists all over the world to agree on an international soil correlation system.

In South Asia agricultural research is centred mainly on increased output from croplands and from pastures. Vast semiarid areas which have scarcely been touched by man are now being studied to evaluate their development potential for irrigated agriculture. Many experts under international and bilateral programmes are assisting the governments in this task. This continental soils study attempts to present a synthesis of the knowledge available at the present stage of development of soil science in South Asia. It is hoped that it will promote better understanding among soil scientists, planners and farmers, provide useful coordination of national and international soils work and stimulate research and its application in the region.

Value and limitations of the map

The Soil Map of South Asia is meant to be a source of factual data, providing a basis and framework for further regional and national soil surveys at a more detailed scale. It may assist in selecting methods for reclamation, crop production, fertilizer application and general use of soils. Until now all attempts to make overall plans or forecasts for agriculture have been hampered by lack of uniformity in the terminology, nomenclature and classification of soils and by the lack of a comprehensive picture of the world's soil resources.

Through a systematic interpretation of the Soil Map of the World it will be possible to appraise the distribution and the production potential of the major soils on a continental basis and to delineate broad priority areas which deserve further study.

This inventory of soil resources will bring to light the limitations and potentialities of the different regions for increased food production.

In addition, a continental soil map such as the Soil Map of South Asia can be a valuable teaching aid for the training of geographers, soil scientists, agronomists and all those who are interested in the study of the environment.'

Although the publication of the map and text marks a significant step forward, it is necessary to point out its inherent limitations. The accuracy and detail of the information which can be shown are obviously limited by the small scale of the map and by the fact that soil data for some areas are scarce because of inadequate field correlation or lack of direct observations. On the other hand, difficulties have arisen in its use for the compilation of the continental map because of the difference in the methods of field and laboratory studies. These limitations may also apply to the interpretative data, since they can only be as accurate as the soils information on which they are based. Yet despite these shortcomings, the Soil Map of South Asia is the most recent and detailed inventory of soil resources based on international cooperation. Its limitations emphasize the necessity of intensifying soil correlation and obtaining better knowledge of the nature and distribution of soils in areas of the subcontinent where information is lacking or inadequate.

Use of the map and explanatory text

Against the background of the topographic base the soil map shows the broad pattern of dominant soils, marked by different colours. Clusters of closely related colours have been used for soils which have similar characteristics, so that major soil regions can be recognized.

More detailed information about each map unit can be derived from the soil association symbols. The composition of the 350 soil associations is given in Table 4 of Chapter 5, where they are listed alphabetically and numerically and are described in terms of climate, natural vegetation, main rocks, and extension. A table showing the composition of the soil associations is also given on the back of the map sheets.

The meaning of the textural and slope classes which accompany the symbols of the map units and the overprints which indicate phases are indicated on the soil map and further described in Chapter 3. The definitions of the soil units involved can be found in Volume I. The profile descriptions and analytical data in the Appendix illustrate and further clarify the soil definitions.

The geographical distribution of the broad soil regions is shown in Figure 6 and discussed in Chapter 5.

For information on the occurrence, land use, limitations, suitabilities and potentialities of the soil units, Chapter 6 should be consulted. Here the specific management problems of the soil units are discussed.

Those who are interested not only in the nature, distribution and suitabilities of the soils (the "agricultural angle"), but also in the natural environment, will find additional reading in Chapter 4. This chapter deals with climate, vegetation, geomorphology and geology and lithology.

2. ACKNOWLEDGEMENTS

The preparation of the Soil Map of South Asia could only have been accomplished with the cooperation of government institutions and many soil scientists.

Those who gave particular help to the project are listed below. Sincere appreciation is also expressed here to all those whom it has not been possible to single out.

Contributors

OFFICIAL AGENCIES

Afghanistan	Soil Department, Land and Water Resources Survey Authority, Ministry of Agriculture and Irrigation, Kabul
Bangladesh	Soils Institute, Ministry of Food and Agriculture, Dacca
Burma	Land Use Bureau and Irrigation Department, Ministry of Lands and Forests, Rangoon
India	All India Soil and Land Use Survey, Indian Agricultural Research Institute, New Delhi
	Indian Photo-Interpretation Institute, Dehra Dun
	Soil Conservation Department, Ministry of Food and Agriculture, New Delhi
Iran	Soil Institute, Ministry of Agriculture, Tehran
Iraq	Section of Soil Survey and Land Classification, Ministry of Agriculture, Baghdad
Israel	Soil Conservation Division, Israel Ministry of Agriculture, Jerusalem
	The Volcani Institute of Agricultural Research, Rehovot
Jordan	Soil Survey Division, Irrigation and Soils Department, Natural Resources Authority, Amman
Lebanon	Institute of Agricultural Research, Ministry of Agriculture, Tel Amara
Nepal	Soil Science Section, Department of Agriculture, Katmandu
Pakistan	Soils Institute, Ministry of Food and Agriculture, Lahore
Saudi Arabia	Ministry of Agriculture and Water, Riyadh
Sri Lanka	Division of Chemistry, Department of Agriculture, Peradeniya
Syria	Directorate of Soils and Chemical Laboratories, Ministry of Agriculture, Damascus
U.S.S.R.	All-Union Society of Soil Scientists

INDIVIDUAL CONTRIBUTORS

(by country to which their work relates)

Afghanistan	R.G. Menon,[1] V. Nasirov,[1] D.M. Noori, Z. Salem, K.N. Satyapal,[1] V.S. Subramanian [1]
Bangladesh	H. Brammer,[1] A. Islam
Burma	B.I. Gasanov,[1] M.F. Purnell,[1] B.G. Rozanov
India	J.S. Bali, J. Bennema,[1] T. Day,[1] J.S. Kanwar, F. Mouttapa,[1] R.S. Murthy, S.V. Govinda Rajan, S.P. Raychaudhuri, T.R. Srinivasan, R.V. Tamhane
Iran	J.R. Desaunettes,[1] M.L. Dewan,[1] J. Famouri, A.F. Mahdavi, P.J. Mahler,[1] L.H.J. Ochtman,[1] M. Vakilian
Iraq	F.H. Altaie, P. Buringh,[1] H.M. Yahia

---

[1] FAO staff.

Israel	J. Dan, H. Koyumdjisky, Z. Raz, D.H. Yaalon
Jordan	D.R. Harris,[1] F.R. Moormann[1]
Lebanon	J.R. Desaunettes,[1] K. Khazzaka, P.J. Mahler,[1] A. Osman, J. Thirion,[1] W. Verheye[1]
Nepal	M. Kaddah, M.L. Pradhan, A. Van Wambeke[1]
Pakistan	M. Bashir, R. Brinkman,[1] J.F. Douglas,[1] P.R. Hesse,[1] G.M. Higgins,[1] A.G. Riaz, M. Rafiq
Saudi Arabia	J.E. Paseur[1]
Sri Lanka	C.R. Panabokke
Syria	W.J. van Liere[1]

Preparation of the map

In close collaboration with the above-listed government institutions, soil specialists and FAO staff, successive soil map drafts of parts of the region were prepared at the FAO project centre in Rome. The first draft of a general soil map of the Near East, compiled from existing maps of separate countries, was assembled in FAO in 1962, and a second draft in 1963. A first draft of a soil map of India was completed in 1968. These drafts were assembled at FAO Headquarters in the overall map of South Asia in 1972, after correlation with the FAO Legend to the Soil Map of the World.

Grateful acknowledgement is made of the permission given by the American Geographical Society of New York to use its 1 : 5 000 000 World Map as a basis for the preparation of the Soil Map of the World.

Preparation of the explanatory text

The technical sections of the draft explanatory text were edited in 1972 by M. Rafiq. H. Brammer contributed to the chapter on Land Use and Soil Suitability. Background information for the sections on Geomorphology, Geology and Lithology was contributed by P.L.J. de Jongh. The final draft of the text was completed and assembled at FAO Headquarters in December 1973.

Financial support

The costs of the preparation and printing of the Soil Map of South Asia were shared by FAO and Unesco. Acknowledgement is also made here to the Government of the Netherlands, which made the services of P.L.J. de Jongh available to the project from 1970 to 1972.

---

[1] FAO staff.

3. THE MAP

Topographic base

The Soil Map of South Asia was prepared on the basis of the 1 : 5 000 000 topographic map series of the American Geographical Society of New York, assuming an average radius of the earth of 6 378 388 metres. For South Asia this map is in two sheets, VII-1 and VII-2, which overlap over Afghanistan and Pakistan. The Miller oblated stereographic projection was used.[1]

Areas of land surfaces measured directly on the map with a planimeter are subject to variations due to the projection of less than 8%. Distances between land points measured directly on the map are subject to errors of less than 4%. Accuracy can be greatly improved by use of the key on the American Geographical Society map, which gives lines of equal scale departure and conversion tables based on mean scale departure ratio.

Map units

The map unit consists of a soil unit or of an association of soil units. The textural class is indicated for the dominant soil unit while a slope class reflects the topography in which the soil association occurs. Furthermore, the associations may be phased according to the presence of indurated layers or hard rock at shallow depth, stoniness, salinity and alkalinity. The soil units, classes and phases are defined in Volume I.

Each soil association is composed of dominant and subdominant soil units, the latter estimated to cover at least 20% of the delimited area. Important soil units which cover less than 20% of the area are added as inclusions.

The symbols of the map units show the soil unit, textural class and slope class as follows:

1. Soil units

The symbols used for representation of the soil units are those shown in Table 1.

---
[1] A bipolar oblique conformal projection is erroneously mentioned on the map sheets.

2. Textural classes

The textural classes, coarse, medium and fine, are shown by the symbols 1, 2 and 3 respectively.

3. Slope classes

The slope classes, level to gently undulating, rolling to hilly, and strongly dissected to mountainous, are indicated by the letters a, b and c respectively.

Cartographic representation

SYMBOLS

The soil associations are noted on the map by the symbol representing the dominant soil unit, followed by a figure which refers to the descriptive legend on the back of the map in which the full composition of the association is outlined.

Examples: Vc50   Chromic Vertisols and Calcic Xerosols

Xk21   Calcic Xerosols, Luvic Xerosols and Lithosols

Associations in which Lithosols are dominant are marked by the Lithosol symbol I combined with one or two associated soil units.

Examples: I-Re-Yh   Lithosols, Eutric Regosols and Haplic Yermosols

I-Yk   Lithosols and Calcic Yermosols

If information on the textural class of the surface layers (upper 30 cm) of the dominant soil is available, the textural class figure (1, 2 or 3) follows the association figure, separated from it by a dash.

Examples: Vc50-3   Chromic Vertisols, fine textured, and Calcic Xerosols

Xk21-3   Calcic Xerosols, fine textured, Luvic Xerosols and Lithosols

Where two groups of textures occur that cannot be delimited on the map, two figures may be used.

Example: Yk40-2/3   Calcic Yermosols, medium and fine textured, and Solonchaks

The slope class of the soil association is indicated by a small letter (a, b or c) immediately following the textural notation.

Example: Vc50-3a Chromic Vertisols, fine textured, and Calcic Xerosols, level to gently undulating

In complex areas where two types of topography occur that cannot be delimited on the map, two letters may be used.

Example: Lc33-3b/c Chromic Luvisols, fine textured, Vertic Cambisols, Rendzinas and Lithosols, rolling to steep

If information on texture is not available, the small letter indicating the slope class will immediately follow the association symbol.

Example: Yk32-a Calcic Yermosols, Lithosols and Luvic Yermosols, level to gently undulating

MAP COLOURS

The soil associations have been coloured according to the dominant soil unit. Each of the soil units used for the Soil Map of the World has been assigned a specific colour. The distinction between map units is shown by a symbol on the map.

The colour selection is made by clusters so that "soil regions" of genetically related soils will show up clearly.

If available information is insufficient to specify the dominant soil unit, the group of units as a whole is marked by the colour of the first unit mentioned in the list (e.g. the colour of the Haplic Yermosols to show Yermosols in general, and the colour of the Dystric Cambisols to show Cambisols in general).

In associations dominated by Lithosols, stripes of grey (the Lithosol colour) alternate with stripes of the colour of the associated soils. If no associated soils are recognized (because they occupy less than 20% of the area or because specific information is lacking), the Lithosol colour is applied uniformly over a striped pattern.

PHASES

Phases are indicated on the Soil Map of South Asia by overprints.

TABLE 1. – SOIL UNITS FOR SOUTH ASIA

J	FLUVISOLS	T	ANDOSOLS	K	KASTANOZEMS	P	PODZOLS
Je	Eutric Fluvisols			Kh	Haplic Kastanozems	Pl	Leptic Podzols
Jc	Calcaric Fluvisols	V	VERTISOLS			Ph	Humic Podzols
Jd	Dystric Fluvisols						
Jt	Thionic Fluvisols	Vp	Pellic Vertisols	H	PHAEOZEMS	W	PLANOSOLS
		Vc	Chromic Vertisols				
				Hh	Haplic Phaeozems	We	Eutric Planosols
G	GLEYSOLS			Hc	Calcaric Phaeozems	Ws	Solodic Planosols
		Z	SOLONCHAKS				
Ge	Eutric Gleysols						
Gc	Calcaric Gleysols	Zo	Orthic Solonchaks	B	CAMBISOLS	A	ACRISOLS
Gd	Dystric Gleysols	Zm	Mollic Solonchaks				
Gm	Mollic Gleysols	Zt	Takyric Solonchaks	Be	Eutric Cambisols	Ao	Orthic Acrisols
Gh	Humic Gleysols	Zg	Gleyic Solonchaks	Bd	Dystric Cambisols	Af	Ferric Acrisols
Gp	Plinthic Gleysols			Bh	Humic Cambisols	Ah	Humic Acrisols
Gx	Gelic Gleysols			Bg	Gleyic Cambisols	Ap	Plinthic Acrisols
		S	SOLONETZ	Bk	Calcic Cambisols	Ag	Gleyic Acrisols
				Bc	Chromic Cambisols		
R	REGOSOLS	So	Orthic Solonetz	Bv	Vertic Cambisols		
		Sg	Gleyic Solonetz	Bf	Ferralic Cambisols	N	NITOSOLS
Re	Eutric Regosols						
Rc	Calcaric Regosols					Ne	Eutric Nitosols
Rd	Dystric Regosols	Y	YERMOSOLS	L	LUVISOLS	Nd	Dystric Nitosols
						Nh	Humic Nitosols
		Yh	Haplic Yermosols	Lo	Orthic Luvisols		
I	LITHOSOLS	Yk	Calcic Yermosols	Lc	Chromic Luvisols		
		Yy	Gypsic Yermosols	Lk	Calcic Luvisols	F	FERRALSOLS
Q	ARENOSOLS	Yl	Luvic Yermosols	Lv	Vertic Luvisols		
		Yt	Takyric Yermosols	Lf	Ferric Luvisols	Fo	Orthic Ferralsols
Qc	Cambic Arenosols			Lp	Plinthic Luvisols	Fr	Rhodic Ferralsols
Qf	Ferralic Arenosols			Lg	Gleyic Luvisols	Fh	Humic Ferralsols
Qa	Albic Arenosols	X	XEROSOLS			Fp	Plinthic Ferralsols
E	RENDZINAS	Xh	Haplic Xerosols	D	PODZOLUVISOLS	O	HISTOSOLS
		Xk	Calcic Xerosols				
		Xy	Gypsic Xerosols	De	Eutric Podzoluvisols	Oe	Eutric Histosols
U	RANKERS	Xl	Luvic Xerosols	Dd	Dystric Podzoluvisols	Od	Dystric Histosols

NOTE: This table follows the order of presentation of soil units in Volume I.

The *petric, petrocalcic* and *petrogypsic* phases show the presence of indurated layers (concretionary horizons, petrocalcic and petrogypsic horizons respectively) within 100 cm of the surface.

The *stony* or *gravelly* phase marks areas where the presence of gravel, stones, boulders or rock outcrops makes the use of mechanized agricultural equipment impracticable.

A *lithic* phase indicates shallow soils with an average depth of 10 to 50 cm.

The overprint representing *shifting sands* has been used locally with sandy Regosols or Arenosols to indicate that a significant part of the area consists of shifting dunes.

The *saline* phase shows that certain soils of the association (not necessarily the dominant ones) are affected by salt to the extent that they have a conductivity greater than 4 mmhos/cm in some part of the soil within 125 cm of the surface for some part of the year. The phase is intended to mark present or potential salinization. The *sodic* phase is used for soils which have more than 6% saturation with sodium in some part of the soil within 125 cm of the surface. It should be noted that Solonchaks are not shown as saline phases, nor Solonetz as sodic phases, since these soils are saline and sodic respectively by definition. It follows that to identify all areas with saline soils one should include saline phases plus Solonchaks, and that areas with alkali soils include sodic phases plus Solonetz.

Where more than one of these phases applies, the phase causing the strongest limitations for agricultural production has been shown. In some cases the lithic and stony phases have been shown together.

MISCELLANEOUS LAND UNITS

Miscellaneous land units are used to indicate salt flats, dunes and shifting sands, and glaciers and snow caps.

Where the extent of the land unit is large enough to be shown separately the sign may be printed over a blank background. In case the land unit occurs in combination with a soil association the sign may be printed over the colour of the dominant soil.

Sources of information

A map showing the sources of information of the Soil Map of South Asia is shown as an inset on the soil map. A separation is made between the areas compiled from systematic soil surveys, soil reconnaissance, and general information supplemented by occasional local field observations.

About 14% of the subcontinent is now covered by soil survey maps based on sufficient ground control to be placed in reliability class I. Inevitably, among these maps there is variation in accuracy depending on a number of factors such as scale, methodology and purpose of preparation. The use of diverse methods of classification also makes correlation more difficult and reduces the reliability of the map. Further uncertainty is introduced by the influence on soil boundaries of differing concepts used in defining the units.

Approximately 22% of the soil map in reliability class II has been prepared from soil reconnaissance designed to give, in combination with basic information on the natural environment, a fair idea of the composition of the soil pattern. Advantage was taken of marked changes in the vegetational, geomorphological, lithological and climatic patterns in the preparation of the soil maps of certain areas where coverage by soil surveys was insufficient.

Reliability class III, covering 64% of the subcontinent, refers to areas which are unexplored, or in which occasional soil studies have not supplied sufficient basic data for the compilation of more than a rough sketch of the soil pattern, even at the 1 : 5 000 000 scale. To understand the soil pattern of these regions, therefore, further studies still need to be undertaken. Aerial photographs are seldom available. However, since these regions are mostly thinly populated and have poor accessibility, they usually have a low priority position for development. It may take a long time before the necessary data for appreciably improving the map are at hand. New aerial photographs and other information that may become available through remote sensing from spacecraft and satellites may eventually be used.

In the preparation of the Soil Map of South Asia a large number of documents was consulted. Although it is impossible to mention all of them, the main ones, covering substantial areas of the map or specifically prepared for the project, are recorded here by the country of origin. Comment is also made on the reliability of the maps in the areas discussed.

AFGHANISTAN

The main source of information was a general soil map of Afghanistan at 1 : 2 000 000 scale compiled in 1962 by V. Subramanian of FAO, who completed a three-year assignment in Afghanistan with the FAO/UNDP Survey of Land and Water Resources Project. The project systematic survey programme was concentrated in areas with irrigation development potential, e.g. the Hari Rud and Farah Rud valleys and the Kabul, Ghazni and Nahar basins, totalling 1.7 million hectares. The total area covered by systematic soil surveys in Afghanistan amounts to some 6 million hectares. The remaining area of the country was mapped by interpretation of data available from findings in the surveyed areas.

BAHRAIN

The main source of information was the general soil map of the Arabian Peninsula drafted in 1971 by J.E. Paseur of FAO. The map was based on the Geological Map of the Arabian Peninsula prepared by the U.S. Geological Survey and the Arabian-American Oil Company in 1963.

BANGLADESH

A soil map of the country was compiled in 1970 on the basis of the findings of the FAO/UNDP Soil Survey Project, Pakistan. The project started in 1961 and its main purpose was to provide a semi-detailed soil survey of the agricultural areas of the then West and East Pakistan. A major part of the area of the country was surveyed during the project and the general soil map contributed to the Soil Map of the World therefore has a high level of reliability.

BURMA

A reconnaissance soil map of Burma at 1 inch to 40 miles scale (approximately 1 : 2 500 000) was prepared by B.G. Rozanov and published in 1959 by the Soils and Land Use Bureau. A first correlation of the map units with FAO legend was attempted by B.I. Gasanov of FAO, who was assigned to the country from 1967 to 1970. The final draft of the country map incorporating recent information was compiled with the assistance of M.F. Purnell, another FAO soil survey specialist working in the country at the time of finalization of the present text and map.

INDIA

A soil map of India was presented by S.P. Raychaudhuri at the Soil Correlation Seminar for South and Central Asia held in Tashkent, U.S.S.R., in 1962. At about the same time another soil map was published by S.V. Govinda Rajan. In 1965, a draft soil map of the country at 1 : 3 000 000 scale was prepared by the All India Soil and Land Use Survey as background material for the soil correlation and appraisal meeting in New Delhi. The International Soil Map of Vegetation, published in Bombay in 1965 by the Indian Council of Agricultural Research,

SOURCES OF INFORMATION

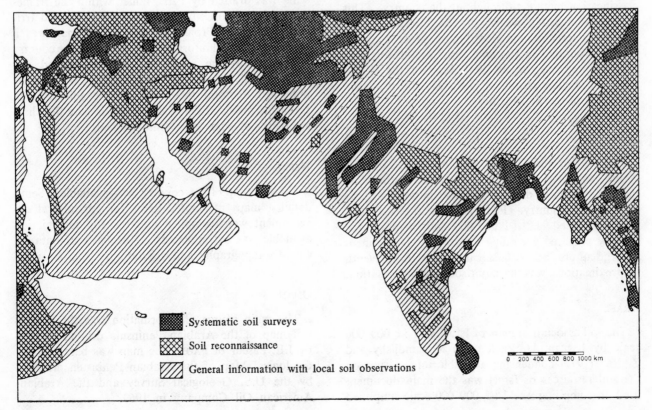

Systematic soil surveys

Soil reconnaissance

General information with local soil observations

0 200 400 600 800 1000 km

also contributed valuable information on soil distribution in the southern part of the subcontinent.

All this material, including the map of Asia at 1 : 6 000 000 scale published by the Dokuchaiev Institute, was compiled and correlated, and a first draft of a soil map of India, based on FAO units, was completed in 1968. This draft was later amended to incorporate new information obtained from FAO/UNDP field projects, especially in the Rajasthan canal area.

IRAN

A soil map of Iran at 1 : 2 500 000 scale was compiled in the late 1950s with the assistance of M.L. Dewan, an FAO soil specialist assigned to the country from 1953 to 1959. The map, published in 1961 by the Soil Department of the Ministry of Agriculture and FAO, was followed by *The Soils of Iran*, published by FAO in 1964.

Soil surveys and land resources studies were considerably expanded from 1966 onward, with the establishment of the Soil Institute with the assistance of FAO and UNDP. The Soil Institute was entrusted with all soil studies in the country. Soil surveys of some 70 areas selected for agricultural development were carried out, and interpretative land evaluation studies covered some 12 million hectares in the northwestern part of the country. A soil correlation programme was also initiated to standardize classification methods throughout the country. This project produced a wealth of new information on soil characteristics and distribution in Iran which was incorporated in the final draft of the soil map of Iran prepared for the Soil Map of the World with the collaboration of J.R. Desaunettes, soil correlator of the Soil Institute.

IRAQ

P. Buringh's study (1960) containing a 1 : 1 000 000 general soil map of Iraq was extensively utilized in the compilation of data on soil distribution and land use in the country. F.H. Altaie's thesis (1968), which included a 1 : 1 000 000 soil map of the country prepared according to the U.S. Department of Agriculture Soil Classification System (Seventh Approximation), was the major source of information.

ISRAEL

The soil association map of Israel at 1 : 1 000 000 scale by J. Dan, D. Yaalon, H. Koyumdjisky and Z. Raz (1972) condensing available information on the soil resources of Israel was the main document used in compiling the 1 : 5 000 000 scale simplified map. The Israel Journal of Earth Science has published an explanatory booklet supplementing the map by Dan *et al*. The booklet presents a tentative correlation of the soil units of the Israeli classification with the U.S. Department of Agriculture and FAO nomenclatures.

JORDAN

A general soil map of Jordan at 1 : 2 000 000 scale by F.R. Moormann of FAO (1959) was used as basic information. The detailed information on soils of limited areas selected for irrigation or range development projects which has become available during the last ten years was fully utilized in the compilation of the final document.

KUWAIT

The main source of information was the general soil map of the Arabian Peninsula drafted in 1971 by J.E. Paseur of FAO. The map was based on the Geological Map of the Arabian Peninsula prepared by the U.S. Geological Survey and the Arabian-American Oil Company in 1963.

LEBANON

A soil resources map of Lebanon at 1 : 250 000 scale was drafted by P.J. Mahler within the framework of an FAO/UNDP Soil Survey and Related Irrigation Schemes Project in 1967. This map was a compilation of all information available in the country and especially the results of the semidetailed surveys carried out during the project. Two recently published doctoral theses on specific soil research problems provided detailed information on the characteristics of some representative soils.

NEPAL

No soil map of the country was available. Semidetailed maps of limited areas for agricultural development were compiled and the soil information available was extrapolated on the basis of data on climate, topography and vegetation.

OMAN

The main source of information was the general soil map of the Arabian Peninsula drafted in 1971 by J.E. Paseur of FAO. The map was based on the Geological Map of the Arabian Peninsula prepared by the U.S. Geological Survey and the Arabian-American Oil Company in 1963.

PAKISTAN

The main source of information was the general soil map of the country at 1 : 5 000 000 scale included in the report of the FAO/UNDP Soil Survey Project, Pakistan, published by FAO in 1971. The project lasted about nine years, during which extensive agricultural areas in the Indus plains were surveyed. Small areas of rangeland and forests were also surveyed. The mountains and desert areas were mapped partly in broad reconnaissance, and partly by using available information.

PEOPLE'S DEMOCRATIC REPUBLIC OF YEMEN

The main source of information was the general soil map of the Arabian Peninsula drafted in 1971 by J.E. Paseur of FAO. The map was based on the Geological Map of the Arabian Peninsula prepared by the U.S. Geological Survey and the Arabian-American Oil Company in 1963.

QATAR

The main source of information was the general soil map of the Arabian Peninsula drafted in 1971 by J.E. Paseur of FAO. The map was based on the Geological Map of the Arabian Peninsula prepared by the U.S. Geological Survey and the Arabian-American Oil Company in 1963.

SAUDI ARABIA

The main source of information was the general soil map of the Arabian Peninsula drafted in 1971 by J.E. Paseur of FAO. The map was based on the Geological Map of the Arabian Peninsula prepared by the U.S. Geological Survey and the Arabian-American Oil Company in 1963. The part of the soil map covering western Saudi Arabia was also based on data available from the resources survey project in Saudi Arabia executed by three private consulting firms: Italconsult, SOGREAH, and Parson/Basil Consult.

SRI LANKA

A general soil map of the great soil groups of the country at 1 : 500 000 scale was published in 1962 by the Land Use Division of the Department of Agriculture and was reprinted with minor changes in 1967. A Colombo Plan survey of the Walawe Ganga basin provided detailed information on the soils of the project area.

SYRIA

The soil map of Syria at 1 : 500 000 scale, published in 1963 with the assistance of FAO soil specialist W.J. van Liere, was used as the basic document. The map units of this map are at great group level, and correlation with FAO soil units was based on profile descriptions and more detailed surveys of specific project areas. Separation of Yermosols from Xerosols in the southern part of the country was largely based on climatic data.

UNITED ARAB EMIRATES

The main source of information was the general soil map of the Arabian Peninsula drafted in 1971 by J.E. Paseur of FAO. The map was based on the Geological Map of the Arabian Peninsula prepared by the U.S. Geological Survey and the Arabian-American Oil Company in 1963.

YEMEN ARAB REPUBLIC

The main source of information was the general soil map of the Arabian Peninsula drafted in 1971 by J.E. Paseur of FAO. The map was based on the Geological Map of the Arabian Peninsula prepared by the U.S. Geological Survey and the Arabian-American Oil Company in 1963.

References

MAPS

Geological map of the Arabian Peninsula, 1:2 000 000. U.S.
1963 Geological Survey and the Arabian-American Oil Company.

General soil map of Afghanistan by V. Subramian. Scale
1962 1:2 000 000.

General soil map of Ceylon by C.R. Panabokke. Scale 1:500 000.
1962 Land Use Division, Department of Agriculture.

PUBLICATIONS

ALTAIE, F.H. The Soils of Iraq. Ghent, State University of
1968 Ghent. (Thesis) (Mimeographed)

ALTAIE, F.H., SYS, C. & STOOPS, G. Soil groups of Iraq,
1969 their classification and characterization. Pedologie,
19(1): 65-148.

BURINGH, P. Soils and soil conditions in Iraq. Baghdad,
1960 Ministry of Agriculture.

CANADA-CEYLON COLOMBO PLAN PROJECT. Report on a re-
1960 connaissance survey of the resources of the Walawe
Ganga basin. Colombo, Government Press.

DEVELOPMENT AND RESOURCES CORPORATION. Kunduz-Khan
1971 Abad irrigation feasibility study, Afghanistan. Final
report. Appendix 1. Rome. FAO/UNDP Project (AFG
68/520).

DEWAN, M.L. & FAMOURI, J. The soils of Iran. Rome, FAO.
1964 FAO and Soil Institute of Iran.

FAO. *Report to the Government of Nepal on soil survey inves-*
1965 *tigations and soil analysis*. Rome. FAO/EPTA Report No. 2043.

FAO. *Enquête pédologique et programmes d'irrigation connexes*
1968 *au Liban. Rapport final*. Rome. Projet FAO/PNUD (LEB/10).

FAO. *Soil resources in West Pakistan and their development*
1971 *possibilities*. Rome. FAO/UNDP Soil Survey Project, Pakistan (PAK/59/506). Technical Report No. 1.

FAO. *Soil survey and soil and water management research and*
1972 *demonstration in the Rajasthan canal area. Terminal Report*. Rome. FAO/UNDP Project (IND/65/524).

FAO. *Soil survey, classification and land evaluation*. Rome.
1972 Technical report No 1. FAO/UNDP (IRA/66/518). Soil Institute of Iran and Associated Pilot Development Project.

FAO. *Investigation of the sandstone aquifers of east Jordan.*
1972 *Technical report on soil studies and land classification of the agricultural development areas*. Rome. FAO/ UNDP Project (JOR/65/509).

FISHER, W.B. *et al. Soil and land potential survey of the high-*
1967 *lands of northwest Jordan*. Durham, University of Durham, Department of Geography.

FRASER, I.S. *Report on a reconnaissance survey of the landforms,*
1958 *soils and present land use in the Indus plains, Pakistan.* Colombo Plan Cooperative Project. Published for the Government of Pakistan by the Government of Canada.

GASANOV, B.I. *Report to the Government of Burma on soil*
1971 *survey*. Rome. FAO/UNDP. TA Report No. 2944.

GAUSSEN, H. *et al. Carte internationale du tapis végétal, notice*
1968 *de la feuille*. Kathiawar, Institut français de Pondi-chéry.

HUNTING TECHNICAL SERVICES LTD. Kerak-Hasa ground-
1968 water irrigation project. Volume 2. *Soils and Agriculture*. Amman, Natural Resources Authority.

HUNTING TECHNICAL SERVICES LTD. & SIR M. MACDONALD &
1966 PARTNERS. *Lower Indus report*. Lahore, WAPDA Printing Press.

INTERNATIONAL ENGINEERING CO. INC. *Report to the Royal*
1959 *Government of Afghanistan on soils and water resources of southwest Afghanistan*. Vol. 2, *Project Areas*. San Francisco, California.

KORLOVSKY, F.I. *Condition actuelle des terres irriguées de la*
1969 *vallée de l'Euphrate. Rapport au Gouvernement de la République syrienne*. Rome. FAO/PNUD Report AT No. 2614.

MOORMANN, F.R. *Report to the Government of Jordan on the*
1959 *soils of east Jordan*. Rome. FAO/ETAP Report No. 1132.

MOORMANN, F.R. & PANABOKKE, C.R. *Soils of Ceylon,*
1961 Colombo, Government Press. FAO and Land Use Division, Department of Agriculture.

NIPPON-KOEI. *Report on the soil survey in Birganj-Gandak*
1972 *irrigation project. Technical Report*. Tokyo. FAO/ UNDP Project (NEP/66/507).

OSMAN, A. *Contribution à l'étude des sols du Liban nord.*
1971 Gand, Université de l'Etat à Gand. (Thèse) (Polycopié)

PRADHAN, M.L. *et al.* Various soil survey reports: Morang, Sunsari, Jhapa, Banke and Dhanukha districts. Nepal, Department of Agriculture, Soil Science Section.

PURNELL, M.F. *Soil and land classification for irrigation of*
1971 *the Sinthese project, Burma*. Rangoon. FAO/UNDP Sittang Valley Development Project (BUR/68/513). (Mimeographed)

RAYCHAUDHURI, S.P. *et al. Soils of India*. New Delhi,
1963 Indian Council of Agricultural Research.

RAYCHAUDHURI, S.P. & GOVINDA RAJAN, S.V. Soil genesis
1971 and classification. Chapter 5, *Review of Soil Research in India*.

ROZANOV, B.G. *Explanatory note to the soil map of Burma.*
1959 Rangoon, Land Use Bureau. (Mimeographed)

SUBRAMANIAN, V.S., NASIROV, V. & SALEM, Z. General soil
1962 map of Afghanistan. [*Report of the*] *First Soil Correlation Seminar for South and Central Asia, Tashkent, U.S.S.R., 14 September - 2 October 1962*, p. 56-59. Rome, FAO. World Soil Resources Report No. 4.

SUBRAMANIAN, V.S. *et al. Survey of land and water resources,*
1965 *Afghanistan. Final report*. Volume 4, *Soils*. Rome. FAO/UNDP Project (AFG-2).

VAN LIERE, W.J. *Report to the Government of Syria on the*
1965 *classification and rational utilization of soils*. Rome, FAO. FAO/EPTA Report No. 2075.

VAN WAMBEKE, A. *General reconnaissance soil survey of the*
1965 *Terai plain between the Sapt Kosi and the Kamala rivers. Technical report*. Rome. FAO/UNDP Project (NEP/3).

VERHEYE, W. *Formation, classification and land evaluation*
1972 *of soils in Mediterranean areas, with special reference to the southern Lebanon*. Ghent, State University of Ghent. (Thesis) (Mimeographed)

WEST BENGAL. DIRECTORATE OF AGRICULTURE. *Classification,*
1965 *composition, and description of soil profiles of West Bengal*. West Bengal. Technical Bulletin No. 6.

WEST BENGAL. DIRECTORATE OF AGRICULTURE. *A report on*
1966 *the soil work in West Bengal*, Vol. 3. West Bengal.

YAHIA, H.M. *Soils and soil conditions in sediments of the*
1971 *Ramadi province, Iraq*. Amsterdam, University of Amsterdam.

In this chapter brief outlines are given of four aspects of the environment that are important in the development and use of soils: vegetation, geomorphology, geology and lithology.

These outlines indicate the location and nature of the major regions in which important variants of climate, vegetation, landscape and rock types occur. Small-scale maps illustrating these environmental factors appear at the back of this volume.

CLIMATE

Climatic factors

The climate of South Asia is basically determined by latitudinal position and general atmospheric circulation, but is modified by topographical conditions and the interaction between land and sea. The great size of the Asian land mass is an important factor influencing the climate of the area. The central part of Asia has a continental climate which shows great differences in summer and winter temperatures, forming a large high-pressure zone in the winter and a low-pressure zone in the summer. These conditions accentuate the north-south movement of the global pressure zones, the intertropical convergence zone and the subtropical high-pressure belt.

The climate of the area is discussed here in terms of general atmospheric circulation (monsoons, Mediterranean disturbances) and climatic elements (rainfall, storms, temperatures). A classification of the area into various climatic and ecological regions is given at the end of this section.

The circulation of air over South Asia is influenced by the monsoons in the eastern half of the subcontinent (from Burma to Pakistan), and the Mediterranean disturbances in the western half.

As the intertropical convergence zone moves northward with the advance of summer, the temperature over the land rises so that by the end of May the region of highest air temperature and lowest atmospheric pressure lies over northwestern India and adjoining areas of Pakistan (Randhawa, 1958). This low-pressure system takes control of air currents over Asia. The easterly trade winds change direction and become southwesterlies and westerlies upon crossing the Equator. After entering the Arabian Sea and the Bay of Bengal they appear on the west coasts of India and Burma as southwest *monsoons*. The monsoons start in early summer in Sri Lanka and southern India and progressively later in northern India and Pakistan. By June they are well established. The Arabian Sea branch of the monsoon brings copious precipitation on the west coast of Sri Lanka and in India as it hits the Western Ghats mountain range and continues its advance eastward across southern and central India, giving only moderate rainfall. The Bay of Bengal branch causes heavy precipitation in the coastal area of Burma and parts of northeastern India. It is then deflected by the Arakan Yoma mountains and moves northwestward along the Himalayas. It meets the Arabian Sea branch north of the low-pressure area and continues its advance westward, occasionally reaching Kabul and Quetta. As a result, the submountain tract along the Himalayas receives considerable rainfall. The monsoons also give a little rain in the southern part of the Arabian Peninsula and in southern Iran.

The monsoon does not behave as a steady phenomenon. The currents pulsate with a series of eastern depressions originating in or reviving over the head of the Bay of Bengal and moving in a westerly to northwesterly direction across northern and central India. Occurring at the rate of three or four per month during the monsoon season, these depressions divert the humid currents into the central and northwestern areas of India, providing a more even distribution of rainfall. In some years their frequency is low. The rainfall is then confined to the mountain ranges, while the plains of northern and central India suffer from drought. However, the Rajputana region of India and the southern Punjab and Sind plains of Pakistan remain out of the path of the monsoon and get little rain.

By mid-September the southwest monsoon rapidly withdraws from the area, gradually allowing the

TABLE 2. – KEY TO CLIMATIC MAP OF SOUTH ASIA (FIGURE 1)

Map Symbol	Climate	Temperature regimes	Humidity regimes	Main locations
1.1	Humid semihot equatorial	Eq	HU Hu	Western Ghats, India; Sri Lanka; southern Burma
1.2	Humid semihot tropical	Tr	HU Hu	Southern Bangladesh
1.3	Dry semihot tropical	Eq Tr	MO (HI 0.44-1)	Sri Lanka
1.4	Hot tropical	EQ TR	MO Mo	Southwestern and southeastern India; southern and central Burma
1.5	Semiarid tropical	EQ Eq TR Tr	mo	Southern India
1.7	Humid tierra templada	Tt tt	MO	Southern India; central Sri Lanka
1.8	Dry tierra templada	Tt tt	Mo mo	Central Yemen Arab Republic
1.9	Cool winter hot tropical	tr	HU Hu MO Mo mo	India; Bangladesh
2	Tierra fría	TF Tf tf An an aP ap aF	HU Hu MO Mo mo	Sub-Himalayan tract; southwestern Saudi Arabia; central Yemen Arab Republic; mountain region of Sri Lanka
3.1	Hot tropical desert	EQ TR tr	da de di do	Southern Saudi Arabia; southern United Arab Emirates; Oman; south coast of People's Democratic Republic of Yemen; west coast of Yemen Arab Republic; south coast of Iran
3.2	Hot subtropical desert	Ts SU	da de di do	Saudi Arabia; northern United Arab Emirates; Iraq; Jordan; southern Syria; southern Iran; southern Afghanistan; central Pakistan
3.7	Continental desert	CO Co co te	da de di do	Iran; northern Afghanistan
4.1	Humid subtropical	SU Su	HU Hu	Caspian coast
4.2	Monsoon subtropical	SU Su	MO Mo mo	Northern India; northern and southern Pakistan
4.3	Hot semitropical	Ts	MO Mo mo	Central India
4.4	Semihot semitropical	Ts	MO Mo mo	Northern Burma
4.5	Semi-Mediterranean subtropical	SU	Mo	Northern Pakistan
6.1	Subtropical Mediterranean	SU Su	ME Me	Mediterranean coast
6.5	Temperate Mediterranean	TE	ME Me	Western Syria; Lebanon
6.6	Cold temperate Mediterranean	Te te Po Pa pa	ME Me	Northern Iran
6.7	Continental Mediterranean	CO Co co	ME Me	Iran; Afghanistan
6.8	Subtropical semiarid Mediterranean	SU Su Tr tr MA	me	Israel; northwestern Jordan; northern Syria; northern Iraq; western Iran
6.9	Continental semiarid Mediterranean	CO Co co TE Te te	me	Western and northern Iran
8.3	Cold continental	co	HU Hu MO	Elburz mountains, Iran
9.1	Warm steppe	CO	St	Northern Pakistan
9.8	Monsoon continental	CO Co co	Mo mo	Himalayan tract
10.5	Alpine	Al al	HU Hu	Himalayan tract

SOURCE: Papadakis, 1966.

KEY TO TEMPERATURE REGIMES

Temperature regime [1]	Winter type	Summer type
Equatorial		
EQ (Hot equatorial)	Ec	G
Eq (Semihot equatorial)	Ec	g
Tropical		
TR (Hot tropical)	Tp	G
Tr (Semihot tropical)	Tp	g
tR (Cool winter hot tropical)	tP	G g
tr (Cool tropical)	tp	O g
Tierra templada		
Tt (Tierra templada)	Tp tP tp	c
tt (Cool tierra templada)	tp	T
Tierra fría		
TF (Low tierra fría)	Ct or colder	g
Tf (Medium tierra fría)	Ci or colder	O M
tf (High tierra fría)	Ci or colder	T t
Andean [1]		
An (Low Andean)	Ti or milder	A
an (High Andean)	Ti or milder	a
aP (Andean taiga)	Ti or milder	P
ap (Andean tundra)	Ti or milder	p
aF (Andean subglacial desert)	Ti or milder	F
Subtropical		
Ts (Semitropical)	Ct	G f
SU (Hot subtropical)	Ci Av	G
Su (Semihot subtropical)	Ci	g
Marine		
MA (Warm marine)	Ci	O M
Temperate		
TE (Warm temperate)	av Av	M
Te (Cool temperate)	ti Ti	T
te (Cold temperate)	ti Ti	t
Pampean-Patagonian [1]		
Pa (Patagonian)	Tv av Av	t
pa (Cold Patagonian)	Ti av	P
Continental		
CO (Warm continental)	Av or colder	g G
Co (Semiwarm continental)	Ti or colder	M O
co (Cold continental)	pr Pr	t
Polar		
Po (Taiga)	ti or colder	P
Alpine		
Al (Low alpine)	Pr ti Ti	A
al (High alpine)	Pr ti Ti	a

NOTE: "Andean" and "Pampean-Patagonian" refer to climatic types of the Andes, the pampas and Patagonia, not to parts of South Asia locally known by these terms.

KEY TO CLIMATE SYMBOLS

Winter types [1]

Ec   Sufficiently warm for equatorial crops (rubber, coconut)

Tp   Colder but frostless, too warm for cryophilous crops (wheat)

tP   *Idem*, but wheat is not entirely excluded

tp   *Idem*, but sufficiently cool for many cryophilous crops

Ct   Nonfrostless, but sufficiently mild for citrus, marginal for cryophilous crops

Ci   *Idem*, but sufficiently cool for cryophilous crops

Av   Colder, but sufficiently mild for winter oats

av   *Idem*, but winter days are cooler

Tv   Colder, but sufficiently mild for winter wheat

Ti   Colder, but sufficiently mild for winter wheat

ti   Colder, but sufficiently mild for winter wheat

Pr   Too cold for winter wheat; all crops sown in spring

pr   Too cold for winter wheat; all crops sown in spring

Summer types [1]

G   Sufficiently warm for cotton, summer days very hot

g   *Idem*, but summer days less hot.

c   Sufficiently warm for maize and cotton, summer days not so warm, nights cool but frostless all year round

O   Cooler, but sufficiently warm for rice

M   Cooler, but sufficiently warm for maize

T   Cooler, but sufficiently warm for wheat

t   *Idem*, but the frost-free season is shorter

P   Cooler, but sufficiently warm for forest

p   Insufficiently warm for forest and grass but sufficiently warm for tundra

A   More frosty, but sufficiently warm for grassland

a   *Idem*, but frosts in all months

F   Insufficiently warm for tundra but not continuous frost

f   Ice cap

Humidity regimes [1]

HU   Ever-humid

Hu   Humid

ME   Moist Mediterranean

Me   Dry Mediterranean

me   Semiarid Mediterranean

MO   Moist monsoon

Mo   Dry monsoon

mo   Semiarid monsoon

St   Steppe

Si   Semiarid isohygrous

da   Absolute desert

de   Mediterranean desert

di   Isohygrous desert

do   Monsoon desert

[1] Meteorological definitions appear in Papadakis, 1966.

northeasterly air current to assume full sway over the subcontinent and adjoining areas by January. The northeast monsoon is associated with rainy weather over southeastern and southern India from November to January. It brings some rain in northern India, northwestern Pakistan and eastern Afghanistan.

During the transition periods, (April to June and October to December) severe cyclones usually form in the Bay of Bengal and the Arabian Sea. As they move inland they bring heavy rainfall and cause considerable damage owing to high winds and occasional tidal waves in coastal areas. On the average, one or two severe cyclones may be expected in the pre-monsoon period and two or three in the post-monsoon period. Most severely affected are the coastal areas of Bangladesh and India's West Bengal state. The northeasterly winds bring considerable rain in Sri Lanka as well.

The Himalayas play a very important role in the climate of the Indian subcontinent, blocking the cold winds from the north and the monsoon winds from the south. In the summer they influence the formation of low-pressure zones over northwestern India, and by checking the winds from the north they help the monsoons reach more northerly latitudes than would be possible otherwise. The distribution of rainfall is greatly influenced by them.

During the winter the *Mediterranean disturbances* begin to affect the countries west of India with a circulation pattern which is cellular rather than zonal, both at the surface and aloft. The surface circulation is controlled for long periods by the Asian high-pressure system and is dominated by northeasterly winds (Wallen and Brichambaut, 1962). Frequently, however, the cyclones formed on the Mediterranean polar front branch of the mid-latitude westerlies penetrate eastward into the area, breaking down the winter monsoon northeasterlies. The winter circulation of the area west of India can best be described as an interaction between the eastward-moving cyclones and the westerlies from the Mediterranean, which are "blocked" by the Asian high-pressure system extending over Tibet and central Asia (Adle, 1960).

The cyclones gather over the Atlantic or certain favourable regions of the Mediterranean area. They account for almost all the rainfall in the Near East and part of the winter rain in northwestern Pakistan and India. Cyclones from the Mediterranean area move into the Near East on two tracks: south of the Turkish mountains through Syria and north of the Lebanon mountains; and along the Egyptian coast through the Sinai Peninsula toward southern Iraq. 30 to 40 cyclones per year reach Iraq and 20 to 25 get as far as the Iran-Pakistan border.

During the winter Iran is influenced by the northeasterly monsoon circulation, which gives a steady wet season on the windward slopes of the Elburz mountains, where the northeasterlies are orographically lifted. However, precipitation rarely occurs in connection with the northeasterlies on the mountains' leeward slopes in the semiarid Iranian plateau. Precipitation over the Zagros mountains, the Azerbaijan area and the Iranian plateau is exclusively connected with the Mediterranean cyclones which

TABLE 3. – CLIMATIC CHARACTERISTICS OF SOME PLACES REPRESENTING THE VARIOUS ECOLOGICAL REGIONS

Climate	Place	Annual potential evapo-transpiration	Humid-ity index	Leaching rainfall	Humid season [1]	Dry season [2]	Winter type	Summer type	Temper-ature regime	Humid-ity regime
		mm		*mm*						
1.14	Bombay, India	1 190	1.56	1 440	6–9	12–5	Ec	g	Eq	MO
1.12	Colombo, Sri Lanka	940	2.51	1 430	3–12	0	Ec	g	Eq	Hu
1.24	Akyah, Burma	990	5.41	4 610	5–11	1–4	Tp	g	Tr	MO
1.42	Bangalore, India	1 560	0.56	170	7–10	1–4	Tp	G	TR	Mo
1.53	Hyderabad, India	2 050	0.37	130	7–9	11–5	Tp	G	TR	mo
2.13	Katmandu, Nepal	1 200	1.19	750	6–9	11–4	Ci	c	TF	MO
2.41	Nuwara Eliya, Sri Lanka	680	3.36	1 680	3–1	0	Ci	T	tf	Hu
3.12	Muscat, Oman	1 410	0.07	0	0	2–1	Ec	G	EQ	do
3.21	Riyadh, Saudi Arabia	2 750	0.03	0	0	3–2	Ct	G	Ts	da
3.22	Hyderabad, Pakistan	2 550	0.07	0	0	8–7	Ct	G	Ts	do
3.23	Baghdad, Iraq	2 690	0.05	0	0	2–1	Ci	G	SU	da
4.32	Agra, India	2 410	0.28	180	7–8	10–6	Ct	G	Ts	Mo
4.43	Lashio, Burma	1 210	1.31	870	5–10	1–4	Ct	g	Ts	MO
6.15	Beirut, Lebanon	980	0.90	470	11–3	6–9	Ci	g	Su	ME
6.78	Kabul, Afghanistan	1 370	0.25	90	1–4	6–12	Ti	M	Co	Me
6.87	Mosul, Iraq	2 320	0.17	60	12–2	5–11	Av	G	SU	me

SOURCE: Papadakis, 1961.
[1] From month beginning to month ending; 1 is January, 12 is December. 0 means that there is no such season. – [2] From month beginning to month ending; 1 is January, 12 is December. 0 means that there is no such season.

penetrate the area during the winter periods when the blocking effect of the Asian high-pressure system is weak.

As spring approaches, the subtropical branch over the Mediterranean area moves northward with the polar front branch. The frequency of cyclones decreases, but those which do penetrate the area tend to follow the northern track south of the Turkish mountains, and are of great importance because they bring convectional rainfall. In the Azerbaijan area (northwestern Iran) maximum rainfall occurs in April and May. Spring precipitation is quite common, even in the high plateau.

Summer circulation over the Near East has great regularity. The gradual northward movement of the intertropical convergence zone and the warming up of the Asian continent give rise to an extensive low-pressure system with its centre in the rainless deserts of Pakistan. The surface circulation in the Near East is therefore dominated by northwesterly to northerly winds between the subtropical high-pressure system over the Mediterranean on the one hand and the low-pressure system stretching from the Arabian Peninsula to Pakistan on the other. The air masses transported by these winds are very dry, warm and stable, and generally give no precipitation. High relative humidity is experienced in these air masses only on the Mediterranean coast, owing to their passage over the sea. After they pass over the Near Eastern mountains they give some rain and the air is again extremely dry. The upper air circulation over the area in summer is dominated by westerly winds south of the subtropical branch.

Generally speaking, the rainfall decreases eastward from the Mediterranean coast to Pakistan and increases with altitude in Iran and the area west of Iran. The eastward decrease is related to an increase in continentality. However, the rainfall value of the Kirkul-Mosul region of the Iraqi plains is higher than one would expect from the continentality, possibly owing to the cyclones coming in along the main track south of the Turkish mountains.

In the Indian subcontinent the high rainfall areas lie in the northeast and on the west coasts of India and Sri Lanka as well as the coastal area of Burma. A narrow strip along the Himalayas also receives considerable rainfall. The general decrease in rainfall is from east to west and north to south, so that the northwestern part of India and most of Pakistan receive very little rainfall.

The interannual variability increases with decreasing rainfall, as usually occurs. The Mediterranean coast and the slopes of the Elburz and Zagros mountains have low variability. In the Near East the western sides of mountain slopes also have low variability, owing to the steadiness of the westerlies.

The reliability is also related to the increase in marine influence, and altitude has a favourable effect on it. The highest variability occurs in transitional zones between arid and semiarid rainfall areas (200-300 mm) in the Near East.

In India and Pakistan the variability of the monsoon summer rain is considerable, ranging from about 20% in areas receiving more than 1 000 mm normal monsoon rain to about 50% in areas having less than 500 mm rainfall. Such variations result in frequent floods and droughts (Randhawa, 1958).

Thunderstorms, hailstorms and duststorms occur mainly at the beginning and end of the summer monsoon season. Their occurrence is probably related to the shifting of the intertropical front, and their effect on crops is sometimes quite damaging. For example, fruit is often damaged by hailstorms in Kashmir, in the Himachal Pradesh area of India, and in parts of northwesthern Pakistan (Randhawa, 1958).

The mean minimum temperatures during winter are important for winter crops. The number of days with minimum temperatures below 0°C is taken as a frost period (Wallen and Brichambaut, 1962). In Iran, the mountains and the Azerbaijan area have a three- to four-month frost period, from mid-November to mid-March. On the remaining high plateau area the frost period is two to three months (December and January). During the period with mean minimum temperatures between 0°C and + 3°C, frosts are frequent but there is no continuous frost season. Such conditions prevail for about two months in most of the semiarid and arid parts of Jordan and Syria, in the northernmost part of Iraq and in a strip on the western slope of the Zagros mountains.

The western disturbances coming from the Mediterranean area have a warm front and a cold rear. As the front moves eastward over India, it is followed by a cold wave due to the cold dry winds coming from the north or northwest. Frost occurs intermittently during the period from mid-November to mid-February over northern Pakistan and northwestern India.

High summer temperatures occur in the lowlands of Iraq, in Khuzistan and the Iranian high plateaus, and over major parts of Pakistan and India.

Climatic regions

The climatic regions of South Asia are shown in Figure 1. The climatic criteria selected, such as winter severity, duration of the frost-free humid and dry seasons, and potential evapotranspiration, are closely related to crop requirements and distribution, so that the climatic regions delineated by

Papadakis (1961, 1966) are of significance to agriculture.

Each region shown on the map has a number representing the climate. Main climatic characteristics and locations of ecological zones are outlined in Table 2 and the related keys. Climatic data from some representative points of the various regions are given in Table 3.

In the table of soil associations in Chapter 5 the type of climate as characterized in Table 2 and Figure 1 is given for each map unit.

References

ADLE, A.H. *Climats de l'Iran*. Tehran. Publications de
1960 l'Université de Téhéran No. 586.

PAPADAKIS, J. *Climatic tables for the world*. Buenos Aires.
1961

PAPADAKIS, J. *Crop ecologic survey in relation to agricultural*
1965 *development of West Pakistan*, p. 18-21. Rome, FAO.
Draft report PL/ECOL/16.

PAPADAKIS, J. *Climates of the world and their agricultural*
1966 *potentialities*. Buenos Aires.

PAPADAKIS, J. *A sketch of crop ecologic regions of Jordan,*
Lebanon, Syria, Iraq, Kuwait and Iran. Rome, FAO.
Draft report PL/ECOL/9.

RANDHAWA, M.S. *Agriculture and animal husbandry in*
1958 *India*. New Delhi, Indian Council of Agricultural
Research.

WALLEN, C.C. & PERRIN DE BRICHAMBAUT, G. *Technical report*
1962 *on a study of agroclimatology in semiarid and arid zones*
of the Near East. Rome, FAO. FAO/Unesco/WMO
Interagency Project on Agroclimatology.

VEGETATION

The broad vegetation regions

The natural plant cover of South Asia may be divided into 14 main vegetation regions, and subdivided into 34 subregions (Figure 2, which is based on a map drafted by J. Schmithüsen.)[1] These regions are distinguished on the basis of the habitat (either climatic or edaphic), the physiognomy and the structure of the vegetation. In many regions (e.g. central India, Pakistan, Afghanistan and many areas of the Near East), the natural vegetation has been degraded as a result of man's activities or has been completely removed. Thus the vegetation regions

[1] J. Schmithüsen is a lecturer at the Institute of Geography of the University of Saarland in Saarbrücken.

give only a general idea of the natural vegetation, necessary for the study of soils.

The regions are:

1. Tropical wet evergreen forests
   a. Tropical wet forest
   b. Tropical wet evergreen forest

2. Tropical deciduous forests
   a. Tropical deciduous forest
   b. Tropical semievergreen forest

3. Tropical and subtropical mountain forests
   a. Subtropical mountain forest of the eastern Himalayas and Burma
   b. Subtropical mountain forest of the central and western Himalayas

4. Tropical dry forests
   a. Tropical dry forest of southwestern India
   b. Tropical dry forest of central India
   c. Tropical dry forest of Sri Lanka

5. Mediterranean evergreen oak forests
   a. Mediterranean humid oak forest
   b. Mediterranean subhumid oak forest

6. Temperate mountain forests
   a. Temperate humid forest of the eastern Himalayas
   b. Temperate humid forest of the western Himalayas
   c. Temperate humid forest of Iran
   d. Cold temperate forest
   e. Cold temperate oak and juniper forests
   f. Cold temperate oak forest
   g. Temperate dry submountain forest

7. Subalpine and alpine shrub and meadows
   a. Humid alpine and subalpine formations
   b. Dry subalpine shrub and meadows

8. Tropical and subtropical savanna and open forest
   a. Subtropical scrub savanna and open forest
   b. Tropical open forest
   c. Subtropical savanna woodland

9. Mediterranean pseudosteppe and open forest

10. Temperate and Mediterranean steppes
    a. Temperate tree steppe and open forest
    b. Temperate tree steppe with juniper
    c. Temperate mountain steppe
    d. Mediterranean high steppe

11. Semidesert formations
    a. Subtropical semidesert formations
    b. Mediterranean semidesert formations
    c. Temperate semidesert formations

12. Desert formations
   a. Ephemerophyte-dominated formations
   b. Sparse ephemerophytes or no vegetation

13. Mangroves

14. Salt marshes
   a. Littoral salt marshes
   b. Inland salt marshes

1. TROPICAL WET EVERGREEN FORESTS

1a. *Tropical wet forest*

This subregion includes evergreen and semievergreen forest extending over Sikkim; spurs of the eastern sub-Himalayan ranges; the upper Assam, Cachor, upper Brahmaputra and Surma valley regions; the Western Ghats, and a major part of Burma (Randhawa, 1958). This dense, multi-storeyed forest covers areas of up to 1 700 metres altitude. The most conspicuous tropical evergreens are *Michelia champaca, Schima wallichii, Artocarpus chaplasha, Dillenia indica, Talauma hodgsoni,* and *Terminalia* species. At lower elevations *Magnolia* species and *Michelia champaca* are encountered, while at higher elevations *Castanopsis indica, Alnus nepalensis* and *Bucklandia populnea* are found. In the Bengal region, Assam state in India and eastern Nepal the tropical evergreen forest has been mostly replaced by *Shorea robusta* (sal) forest of wet mixed type.

Along the eastern Himalayas and in the upper Brahmaputra and Surma valleys the tropical semievergreen forest comprises the Meliaceae, Lauraceae, Myristicaceae and Manoliaceae families. On the lower slopes the main genera are *Dipterocarpus, Artocarpus, Shorea, Cinnamomum, Dysoxylum, Altingia* and *Mesua. Quercus* species are also found on the lower slopes. In the northern Bengal region the main association is *Schima - Bauhinia* with *Trona, Stereosphermum, Ailanthus, Castanopsis* and *Tetrameles* genera.

In the Western Ghats the main species of the evergreen forest are *Dipterocarpus indicus, Hopea parviflora, H. wightiana, Calophyllum tomentosum, Cullenia rosayroana, Palaquum ellipticum, Dysoxylum malabaricum, Syzygium cumini* and *Actinodaphne ungustifolia.* Among undershrubs *Strobilanthes* is important.

1b. *Tropical wet evergreen forest*

Occupying the southwestern quarter of Sri Lanka, this subregion extends from the plains to altitudes of about 900 metres (Gaussen *et al.*, 1968). The two vegetation associations are *Doona - Dipterocarpus - Mesua* and *Filicium - Euphoria - Artocarpus - Myristica.* The forest is multi-storeyed and quite dense.

In its maximum development the first series represents the best type of forest in Sri Lanka, giving a high timber yield. Its subdivisions are high evergreen forest, low evergreen forest, high thicket, discontinuous thicket and fernland. In the high forest the closed upper storey is 22 to 27 metres high with scattered towering giant trees of 30 to 45 metres. In the best-developed and undisturbed areas the trees are dense enough to form a closed stratum and the undergrowth is thin. In the low forest the upper storey ranges from 9 to 18 metres in height and big trees are rare. Thicket formations develop when areas under shifting cultivation are left fallow for long periods or when the forests surrounded by shifting cultivation areas are overexploited. Fernland develops in areas which are abandoned after many years of cultivation.

The second vegetation series is a transition to deciduous forest consisting of high evergreen forest and semideciduous forest and thicket and savannawoodland formations. In the savanna there is a grass cover about 1 metre high.

2. TROPICAL DECIDUOUS FORESTS

2a. *Tropical deciduous forest*

This moist deciduous forest occurs in the Western Ghats and in northern Uttar Pradesh, Bihar and Assam states in India, as well as in parts of central Burma (Randhawa, 1958). The predominant trees are *Madhuca latifolia, Mangifera indica, Michelia champaca, Polyalthia longifolia* and *Salmolia malabarica.* In the Western Ghats trees such as *Tectona grandis, Dalbergia latifolia* and *Grewia leptopetala* are found.

2b. *Tropical semievergreen forest*

Whereas the upper storey of this forest in Sri Lanka is sparse and discontinuous, the lower stratum is dense and continuous. The vegetation series is *Chloroxylon - Berrya - Vitex - Schleichera* (Gaussen *et al.*, 1968). The main formations are deciduous and semideciduous forests. The deciduous forest is composed of a principal semideciduous or semievergreen closed stratum reaching a height of 18 metres and a more open stratum of larger, predominantly deciduous trees 25 metres high. The semideciduous forest forms after the removal of large valuable deciduous trees. This forest type gives good timber yields. Teak is successfully raised on good soils.

3. TROPICAL AND SUBTROPICAL MOUNTAIN FORESTS

3a. *Subtropical mountain forest of the eastern Himalayas and Burma*

On the lower slopes of the Himalayas in the Bengal region and in India's Assam state there is subtropical mountain forest of tall, predominantly evergreen trees (Randhawa, 1958). At altitudes of 1 700 to 2 700 metres the characteristic trees are *Michelia nilagirica*, *Ternstroemia japonica*, *Eurya japonica*, *Gordonia obtusa* and *Meliosma wightii*. At lower elevations *Mesua*, *Vitex* and *Artocarpus* are found. The undergrowth of ferns is quite dense. Some temperate species are also found.

The birch and oak forests of Burma and Assam state are also included in this subregion.

3b. *Subtropical mountain forest of the central and western Himalayas*

There is dense, open dry forest with *Anogeissus latifolia* and *Shorea robusta* at 500 metres (Randhawa, 1958; Unesco/FAO, 1969). At a higher elevation is sclerophyllous evergreen forest with characteristic *Olea cuspidata*, including degraded formations. From about 800 to 1 800 metres altitude there is open forest with *Pinus longifolia* (*P. roxburghii*) with or without evergreen underwood vegetation.

4. TROPICAL DRY FORESTS

4a. *Tropical dry forest of southwestern India*

This forest occurs in a narrow strip within the damp sea-breeze zone (Randhawa, 1958). The forest type is characterized by low, stunted, dense dry evergreen vegetation of small-leaved and thorny species. The main trees are *Chloroxylon swietenia*, *Diospyros ebenum*, *D. melanoxylon*, *Strychnos nux-vomica* and *Mimusops elengi*. The main shrubs are *Randia*, *Canthium* and *Zizyphus*.

4b. *Tropical dry forest of central India*

This forest, of the mixed moist and dry deciduous type, occupies parts of western Madhya Pradesh, eastern Maharashtra and Andhra Pradesh states. It is mostly a forest of small trees and shrubs occurring with herbaceous vegetation which is leafless or dry in the dry season (Randhawa, 1958). Teak occurs at intervals all over the area except in the south. Typical trees are *Capparis diversifolia*, *Acacia arabica*, *Prosopis spicigera*, *Parkinsonia aculeata* and *Balanites aegyptiaca*. The important species are *Chloroxylon swietenia*, *Pterocarpus santalinus* and *Toona ciliata*.

4c. *Tropical dry forest of Sri Lanka*

Occupying northwestern and southeastern Sri Lanka, this forest occurs at an altitude of less than 300 metres. The vegetation series is *Manilkara - Chloroxylon*, the best stands of which form a closed forest of medium size, 9 to 18 metres high (Gaussen *et al.*, 1968). By overexploitation or shifting cul-

tivation it degrades into a dense thicket 5 to 6 metres high. Tree savanna develops in areas where permanent cultivation has been abandoned, and the establishment of woody species is hindered by fires. This type of forest produces mainly firewood and small-size timber. The Forest Department is planting drought-resistant species of eucalyptus and *Gmelina arborea*.

5. MEDITERRANEAN EVERGREEN OAK FORESTS

5a. *Mediterranean humid oak forest*

This type of forest occurs in the "Fertile Crescent."[2] Forests and degraded forests with *Quercus persica* are found in the south and in the Zagros mountains, *Quercus infectoria* in the north, and *Quercus libani* in the northeast. There are also *Pistacia mutica*, *Pirus syriaca*, *Fraxinus syriaca*, *Amygdalus*, *Hordeum bulbosum*, *Poa bulbosa*, *Aegilops* and some *Stipa* and *Agropyrum*. In Afghanistan there is open forest of *Quercus baloot* (Unesco/FAO, 1969).

5b. *Mediterranean subhumid oak forest*

In the forest on the Caspian coast of Iran *Quercus castaneaefolia* is dominant; other species are *Parrotia persica*, *Gleditschia caspica*, *Zelkova crenata* and *Albizzia julibrissin*. In Azerbaijan, Iran, there are three species of *Quercus*. Included in these is degraded forest with *Oplismenus - Setaria* vegetation (Unesco/FAO, 1969).

6. TEMPERATE MOUNTAIN FORESTS

6a. *Temperate humid forest of the eastern Himalayas*

This type of forest occurs between 2 000 and 3 000 metres altitude in Sikkim, Bhutan, the Balipara frontier tract and associated hill ranges (Randhawa, 1958). Altitude is the main factor influencing the type of vegetation. Between 2 000 and 2 300 metres altitude there is laurel forest with *Machilus*, *Beilschmiedia*, *Cinnamomum*, *Litsaea*, *Michelia* and *Magnolia*. From 2 300 to 2 700 metres there is buk oak forest consisting of *Quercus lamellosa*, *Acer campbellii* and *Castanopsis*. From 2 700 to 3 000 metres a high-level oak forest with *Quercus pachyphylla* intermixed with species of the buk oak association is found.

In Nepal temperate forest is found at elevations of 2 700 metres. The main species are *Quercus lineata*, *Pasania pachyphylla*, *Acer*, *Magnolia*, *Betula* and *Taxus*. Ferns are abundant. Above 3 000 me-

---

[2] Foothill regions of northern Iraq, western Syria and Lebanon.

tres oaks become less abundant and are replaced by pines such as *Picea excelsa*, which are found up to 4 000 metres.

6b. *Temperate humid forest of the western Himalayas*

Oaks and conifers occur from approximately 1 800 to 3 300 metres altitude; salient species are *Quercus incana*, *Q. dilatana*, *Q. semicarpifolia* and *Cedrus deodara*. At the upper limit are *Abies spectabilis*, rhododendrons and *Juniperus* (Unesco/FAO, 1969; Randhawa, 1958).

6c. *Temperate humid forest of Iran*

A forest of *Fagus orientalis*, *Carpinus betulus*, *Acer insigne*, *A. laetum* and *Fraxinus excelsior* occurs from 800 to 2 000 metres altitude on the northern slopes of the Elburz mountains. Also included in this subregion are small areas of dry subalpine stage in the Elburz mountains (Unesco/FAO, 1969).

6d. *Cold temperate forest*

In the Hindu Kush mountains there is an open forest of fir and cedar with *Cedrus deodara*, *Abies webbiana* and *Pinus gerardiana* (Unesco/FAO, 1969).

6e. *Cold temperate oak and juniper forests*

In the Zagros mountains in Iran the forest cover includes *Quercus persica*. This species is found in association with *Q. infectoria* and *Q. libani* in western Kurdistan. Other species are *Pistacia mutica*, *Pirus syriaca*, *Acer cinerascens*, *Celtis*, *Fraxinus*, *Amygdalus* and *Juniperus* on rocky ground. In the valleys there are *Fraxinus oxycarpa*, *Platanus orientalis* and varieties of *Populus*, *Salix* and *Tamarix*. On the southern slopes of the Elburz mountains there is degraded vegetation with *Festuca*, *Astralagus* and *Acanthophyllum*, in association with *Juniperus excelsa* and *Amygdalus* (Unesco/FAO, 1969).

6f. *Cold temperate oak forest*

In Lebanon and on the slopes of the Zagros mountains of Iran there is dense xerophilous oak forest in which *Quercus persica* is dominant. In Lebanon the forest includes small areas of fir and cedar with *Cedrus libani* (Unesco/FAO, 1969).

6g. *Temperate dry submountain forest*

In the Caspian region of Iran there is a forest of *Quercus castaneaefolia*, *Buxus sempervirens* and *Cupressus sempervirens* with *Carpinus* and *Zelkova*. On moist soils *Alnus glutinosa* and *Pterocarya caucasica* occur. In Afghanistan these include pine and oak forests with *Pinus gerardiana* and *Quercus baloot* (Unesco/FAO, 1969).

7. SUBALPINE AND ALPINE SHRUB AND MEADOWS

7a. *Humid alpine and subalpine formations*

The subalpine stage of this subregion in the Himalayas has *Betula utilis* and rhododendrons with an undergrowth of *Abies pindrow* and *Arundinaria aristata*. At the alpine stage there are shrub formations with rhododendrons up to 4 300 metres altitude. Alpine meadows have *Potentilla*, *Anaphalis*, *Androsace*, *Delphinium* and *Rheum* (Unesco/FAO, 1969).

7b. *Dry subalpine shrub and meadows*

This subregion includes the Elburz mountains and small areas in the Zagros and Hindu Kush mountains. The summer is dry. Shrub varieties of *Amygdalus*, *Prunus*, *Daphne*, *Lonicera* and *Rosa* occur up to 3 000 metres altitude. The subalpine meadows have *Bromus tomentellus*, *Agropyrum*, *Poa*, *Festuca ovina*, *Hordeum fragile* and *Juniperus polycarpos* up to 3 800 metres. At 2 000 to 2 700 metres *Betula verrucosa* is found with *Quercus macranthera*, *Acer*, *Juniperus communis*, *J. sabina*, *Lonicera caucasica* and *Carpinus orientalis*. In areas at altitudes of 1 600 to 2 400 metres, where conditions are drier (transitional between humid and dry subalpine), *Quercus macranthera*, *Juniperus communis*, *J. sabina* and *Lonicera caucasica* occur. There is a degraded variant of vegetation with *Astragalus tragacantha* (Unesco/FAO, 1969).

8. TROPICAL AND SUBTROPICAL SAVANNA AND OPEN FOREST

8a. *Subtropical scrub savanna and open forest*

This subregion in Pakistan and India comprises open forest with *Acacia*, degraded open forest with *Acacia*, and open forest with *Anogeissus pendula*.

There is also open forest with *Zizyphus*, *Acacia*, *Calotropis procera* and *Prosopis*. In some areas there are crops under irrigation.

In the Yemen Arab Republic, the People's Democratic Republic of Yemen and Saudi Arabia there is fairly open, dry mountain forest with *Olea chrysophylla* and *Dodonea viscosa*. On the lower and drier mountains there is thorny scrub with *Euphorbia amac* and *Themeda triandra*.

Iran has tree steppe with *Acacia arabica*, *Capparis*, *Acacia seyal*, *Calligonum*, *Zizyphus*, *Euphorbia*, *Cenchrus* and *Hyparrhenia*. In southern Iran, the western hilly region of Pakistan and in Afghanistan, there is

Mediterranean-biased subdesert steppe with *Pistacia khinjuk*, *Amygdalus*, *Acacia* and *Stipa* as well as *Zizyphus*, *Prosopis*, *Calatropis* and *Capparis* (Unesco/FAO, 1969; Randhawa, 1958).

8b.   *Tropical open forest*

This subregion in India and Burma includes savanna formations, most of them degraded (Randhawa, 1958). The most common species are *Anogeissus acuminata*, *A. latifolia*, *Erythrina suberosa*, *Mangifera indica*, *Syzygium cumini* and *Albizzia odoratissima*. The most characteristic trees are *Boswellia serrata* and *Sterculia urens*. Bamboo (*Dendroclamus strictus*) is also found. The lower canopy is comprised of species of *Mallotus*, *Flacourtia*, *Carissa*, *Emblica*, *Wrightia* and *Bauhinia*.

8c.   *Subtropical savanna woodland*

In this subregion in the Arabian Peninsula *Juniperus procera* is more or less dense between 1 800 and 2 000 metres altitude, and *Podocarpus gracilior* is also found (Unesco/FAO, 1969).

9.   MEDITERRANEAN PSEUDOSTEPPE AND OPEN FOREST

This region includes the Zagros mountains, the Fertile Crescent and Pakistan. It comprises pseudosteppe and open forest with *Pistacia atlantica*, *P. khinjuk*, *Amygdalus*, *Tamarix* and *Salix*. In the Near East littoral region there is tree pseudosteppe and open forest with *Pistacia*, *Zizyphus* and *Juniperus* bushes; *Quercus aegilops* occurs in Lebanon. In southern Iran and Baluchistan province in Pakistan there is pseudosteppe with *Artemisia maritima*, *Stipa* and *Cymbopogon* (Unesco/FAO, 1969).

10.   TEMPERATE AND MEDITERRANEAN STEPPES

10a.   *Temperate tree steppe and open forest*

In Iran there is steppe and open forest with *Pistacia mutica* and *P. khinjuk*, which in the north are often shrunken to bush size, with *Amygdalus scoparia* and *A. horrida* dominant. Bush vegetation consists of *Celtis*, *Pirus*, *Crataegus*, *Prunus*, *Daphne* and *Rhamnus*. *Juniperus excelsa* and *Artemisia maritima* - *Stipa barbata* - *S. lagascae* steppe with *Bromus tomentellus* and *Hordeum bulbosum* are found at higher elevations. There is also tree pseudosteppe with *Pistacia*, *Amygdalus* and *Olea*.

In Afghanistan, tree steppe comprises *Artemisia*, *Stipa*, *Pistacia* and a proportion of *Juniperus* and *Amygdalus*. The tree pseudosteppe in the north has *Pistacia khinjuk*, *Amygdalus scoparia* and *Olea cuspidata* (Unesco/FAO, 1969).

10b.   *Temperate tree steppe with juniper*

Afghanistan has tree steppe with relatively dense *Juniperus* cover.

Iran has steppe and open forest with *Juniperus excelsa*, *Amygdalus*, *Celtis* and *Crataegus*, as well as steppe comprising *Artemisia*, *Astragalus*, *Acantholimon*, and *Onobrychis cornuta* (Unesco/FAO, 1969).

10c.   *Temperate mountain steppe*

Afghanistan has steppe with *Artemisia*, *Agropyrum*, *Stipa*, *Astragalus*, *Cousinia* and *Acantholimon*. At high elevations there are some steppes with *Cousinia*, *Astragalus* and *Tragacantha*, and others with *Festuca* and *Cousinia*.

Iran has steppe with *Artemisia maritima* and *Stipa lagascae*, and meadows with *Bromus tomentellus* (Unesco/FAO, 1969).

10d.   *Mediterranean high steppe*

The steppes of Iran and Afghanistan have *Artemisia herba-alba* and *Aristida plumosa* dominants associated with *Haloxylon zygophyllum*, *Stellera lessertii*, *Ephedra*, *Astragalus*, *Acanthophyllum* and others.

Along the east Caspian coast there is subdesert steppe with *Artemisia herba-alba* with *Salsola* and an *Artemisia meyeriana* - *A. fragrans* association.

The Fertile Crescent has tree steppe of varying forest with *Andropogon*, *Dactylis*, *Pistacia*, *Zizyphus lotus* and bushes of *Juniperus excelsa* and *Quercus persica* (Unesco/FAO, 1969).

11.   SEMIDESERT FORMATIONS

11a.   *Subtropical semidesert formations*

Desert and bushes with *Salvadora* and *Acacia* occur in Pakistan.

The Thar desert (India and Pakistan) has steppe with *Calligonum*, *Aerva tomentosa* and others.

In Punjab and Rajasthan states in India there is steppe with *Prosopis spicigera* and *Salvadora oleoides*.

In Iran and Pakistan's Baluchistan province one type of subdesert steppe has *Acacia nubia*, *Acacia seyal*, *Prosopis spicigera*, *Zizyphus spina-Christi*, *Tamarix*, *Salvadora* and *Calatropis*. Another has *Aristida plumosa* on sand and gravel and *Aeluropus repens* on moderately saline soils. Various *Astragalus*, *Echinops*, *Heliotropium*, *Fagonia*, *Stelleria* and *Peganum harmala* are also found. *Tamarix* is confined to the bottoms of wadis. Dunes carry *Arthrophyton persicum* and *Calligonum* species.

The Arabian Peninsula has bush steppes with *Acacia tortilis*, foothills with *Maerua crassifolia*, and sandy plains with *Panicum turgidum* and *Lasiurus*.

There is also steppe with *Artemisia herba-alba* and *Stipa tortilis*.

The Mesopotamian region has steppe with *Artemisia herba-alba* and *Anabasis haussknechtii* (Unesco/FAO, 1969; Randhawa, 1958).

11b. *Mediterranean semidesert formations*

In Iran there are perennial vegetation formations with grass species including *Andropogon*, *Aristida*, *Bromus*, *Cymbopogon*, *Pennisetum* and *Chrysopogon*, and shrubs and bushes of *Acacia*, *Populus*, *Pistacia khinjuk* and *Amygdalus scoparia*. There are also perennial formations with tall grasses such as *Panicum antidotale*, *P. turgidum*, *Pennisetum dichotomum*, *Astragalus fasciculifolius* and *A. squarrosus*. *Stipa capensis*, an annual, is very abundant in overgrazed areas. There is also steppe with *Salsola*.

Syria and the Mesopotamian region have steppe with *Artemisia herba-alba*, *Stipa tortilis* and *Poa sinaica*. In depressions *Zygophyllum dumosum*, *Salsola tetrandra* and *Chenolea arabica* occur.

In the northwestern part of the Arabian Peninsula there is steppe with *Anabasis articulata*, *Artemisia herba-alba* and *Thymelaea hirsuta* (Unesco/FAO, 1969).

11c. *Temperate semidesert formations*

In Iran, Afghanistan and Baluchistan province in Pakistan there is pseudosteppe with *Artemisia*, *Astragalus*, *Acantholimon*, *Arthrophyton*, and *Aristida*. In some places it includes *Haloxylon*, *Zygophyllum*, *Anabasis*, *Pistacia* and *Amygdalus*. In southern parts of the Fertile Crescent *Artemisia herba-alba* and *Anabasis aphylla* are found in arid areas; in the less arid parts the natural vegetation was destroyed by man centuries ago.

In northern Afghanistan *Cousinia* and *Ferula* occur on lowland steppes, and *Carex* and *Astragalus* on sand (Unesco/FAO, 1969).

12. DESERT FORMATIONS

12a. *Ephemerophyte-dominated formations*

In the Arabian Peninsula ephemerophytes are dominant, with some *Haloxylon*, *Rhanterium* and *Salsola* species in depressions (Unesco/FAO, 1969).

12b. *Sparse ephemerophytes or no vegetation*

In Iran, Afghanistan and Baluchistan province in Pakistan there are true deserts with ephemerophytes. *Arthrophyton persicum* and *Calligonum* occur on sand.

In the Rub al-Khali desert (Saudi Arabia) *Calligonum* occurs with ephemeral forms of *Aristida*, *Tribulus* and *Fagonia*.

In the Al-Nafud and Al-Dahana deserts (Saudi Arabia) there are *Calligonum*, *Haloxylon*, *Ephedra* and *Artemisia*.

In the Dasht-e-Lut desert (Iran) there is no vegetation (Unesco/FAO, 1969).

13. MANGROVES

The main species found in the deltas of the Ganges and Irrawaddy rivers are *Rhizophora mucronata*, *Bruguiera gymnorrhiza*, *Sonneratia acida*, *Aegiceras corniculatum*, *Xylocarpa molluccensis*, and *Scyphiphora hydrophyllaceae*. In the Ganges delta some fifty species are found (Randhawa, 1958).

14. SALT MARSHES

14a. *Littoral salt marshes* (Unesco/FAO, 1969).

14b. *Inland salt marshes* (Unesco/FAO, 1969).

References

MAPS

Vegetationskarte. Masstab 1 : 25 000 000. Geographisch-Kartographisches Institut Meyer.

Vegetation map of the Mediterranean zone. Unesco/FAO. 1969 Paris, Unesco.

PUBLICATIONS

GAUSSEN, H. *et al. Explanatory notes on the vegetation map* 1968 *of Ceylon*. An extract from the works of the Technical and Scientific Section of the French Institute in Pondichery, Serial No. 5. Colombo, Government Press.

RANDHAWA, M.S. *Agriculture and animal husbandry in India*. 1958 New Delhi, Indian Council of Agricultural Research.

GEOMORPHOLOGY

South Asia has a great variety of landforms ranging from high mountains to plateaus of various kinds, alluvial plains and sandy deserts. The three main morphostructural regions as distinguished in the description of the geology and lithology of South Asia also represent definite regions (Figure 3) characterized by a distinct landscape development. These regions comprise:

1. The Indian shield and the Indo-Gangetic plain
2. The Arabian shield and the Median zone
3. The Tethys geosyncline

The shield areas of India and Arabia have been stable since the Precambrian and the Cambrian respectively. However, some block movements took place later and large areas in both the shield areas were covered by lava during the Eocene. Erosion has been going on more or less continuously in these areas since the Eocene or before, resulting in the formation of extensive plateaus.

1. THE INDIAN SHIELD AND THE INDO-GANGETIC PLAIN

The major part of the Indian shield is now an undulating plateau about 200 to 1 000 metres above sea level, with some low hills which are barely 500 metres higher than the surrounding land. The plateau consists of a series of peneplains with mesas, buttes and inselbergs (Wadia, 1953). In the level areas of the peneplains weathering has reached great depths and quite an advanced stage. The laterite crust represents the ultimate stage of deep and intensive weathering and is locally found on the remnants of the old peneplain surface which was dissected by later cycles of erosion. In other plain areas, probably on younger peneplain surfaces, Luvisols, Nitosols and Vertisols have developed.

The Assam plateau is a detached part of the Indian shield. It was not affected by the Tertiary folding and has passed through many cycles of erosion. The Shan plateau of Burma is a part of the Sunda shield which extends eastward and has been affected by erosion since the Cretaceous.

The important hill ranges in the Indian shield area are the Western Ghats and the Eastern Ghats, and the Aravalli, Vindhya and Gondwana hills. The Western Ghats are formed of Eocene lava in the north and Precambrian gneiss in the south. They stand about 900 to 1 500 metres above sea level and form a continuous hill range along the west coast that is interrupted only by the Narmada and Tapti troughs, formed by block subsidence. Erosion of the lava hills in the north has carved canyon-like valleys, mesas, buttes and hill pinnacles, producing the characteristic "landing stair" relief. In the gneiss area in the south the hills have somewhat rounded forms.

The Eastern Ghats are not continuous, as they have been cut through by rivers like the Godavari, the Krishna and the Mahanadi, which originate in the Western Ghats and flow eastward. These Ghats are highly dissected and peneplained at about 600 metres height. The Aravalli, Vindhya and Gondwana hill ranges in the north are also highly dissected and have been peneplained at about 700 metres above sea level.

Sri Lanka is part of the Indian shield and has the same history of development of physiographic forms.

The Indo-Gangetic plain occupies a vast geosyncline between the Indian shield and the Himalayas. It has been filled in with the sediments eroded from the mountains since Tertiary times.

2. THE ARABIAN SHIELD AND THE MEDIAN ZONE

The major part of this area comprises plateaus and sand deserts. Mountain ranges cover only a very small part of it.

The Hijaz and the Asir mountains are massifs of Eocene lava and are comparable to the Western Ghats of India. Their considerable altitude (up to 2 700 metres) is probably due to less active weathering in the arid climate. The western slopes of these mountains are steep and are deeply incised by numerous wadis which produce rugged relief. The eastern slopes are gentle and valleys are broad. The Asir mountains form part of a tilted, dissected tableland with an abrupt scarp on the western side and a gentle slope to the east.

Other important mountain ranges include the Lebanon and the Anti-Lebanon occurring along the Mediterranean coast. These are high mountain ranges with precipitous slopes. The Al-Biqa valley which separates them is filled with mainly Pleistocene alluvium.

The plateaus of the Arabian Peninsula, Iraq, Syria, Jordan and Israel are formed generally in horizontal or slightly tilted sedimentary rocks (mostly limestone and sandstone) of Tertiary or Cretaceous age. The deserts are related to the plateaus in age and generally occupy depressions.

The Najd plateau, which extends over a large part of Saudi Arabia, is about 600 metres above sea level. It is formed in Precambrian and Eocene rocks in the western 300-km-wide region, and in Tertiary limestone and sandstone in the eastern part. The Hadhramaut plateau in the southern part of the peninsula is about 1 000 metres high and consists of rolling uplands and some canyons with flat floors up to 300 metres wide. It has a faulted synclinal valley about 300 km long, the upper part of which is wider than the lower. The Al-Summan plateau in northeastern Saudi Arabia is formed in gently tilted sedimentary strata of Eocene-Miocene age. On its level plains a crust of weathered material a few centimetres to less than half a metre thick covers the underlying rock.

A number of plateaus cover northern Saudi Arabia, western Iraq and major parts of Syria and Jordan. Here the surface soil is generally gravelly and stony. The Al-Hamad region consists largely of gravelly and stony plains alternating with belts of sand ridges or sand dunes. In the area bordering the Mesopotamian plain, limestone rock is either close to the surface or exposed. Another rocky plain originates southeast of Damascus and extends into the Arabian Peninsula. Major parts of Jordan, Israel and the Sinai Peninsula are flat and rocky with slightly incised valleys, except the scarp edge bordering the Jordan rift valley, where streams have cut deeply. However, within the rocky areas there are depressions of various sizes where alluvial material has accumulated. In many places the deposit has a loessial character.

Sandy deserts occupy large areas in Saudi Arabia. The Rub al-Khali in the south has vast sand deposits which are mainly aeolian and have been accumulating in this area over a very long geologic period. There are enormous sand ridges which are often more than 40 km long and more than 30 metres high. There are also pyramid dunes up to 200 metres high with base diameters of up to one kilometre. The sand dunes invariably lie on a silty or clayey saline flat, implying playa conditions.

Al-Nafud is another large sandy desert in northern Saudi Arabia, and the long Al-Dahanah desert connects it with the Rub al-Khali. In the Al-Nafud the dunes are 10 to 30 metres high. They are long ridges of sand which alternate with outcrops of horizontal limestone strata.

3. THE TETHYS GEOSYNCLINE

This is an area of young mountains with rugged relief. The upheavals which formed the mountains started in the Eocene and continued in phases up to the beginning of the late Pleistocene (Wadia, 1953). For example, the Himalayas and the Hindu Kush, Elburz and Zagros mountain ranges were mainly uplifted in phases from the Eocene to the Pliocene and the Pleistocene. The central Iranian plateau was formed mainly during the Miocene-Pliocene (Dewan and Famouri, 1964). The Makran ranges, Jabal Barez, the Kirthar range and the Siwalik belt of the Himalayas and the Sulaiman foothills were uplifted during the Pliocene-Pleistocene (Wadia, 1953).

Some parts of the Himalayas were also considerably raised by the upheavals occurring toward the end of the middle Pleistocene. A new cycle of erosion started with each upheaval, so the relief remained young.

As the mountains were being eroded, associated depressions were filled with detritus. The Indo-Gangetic plain, the Dasht-i-Margo desert in Afghanistan and the Dasht-e-Kavir and Dasht-e-Lut deserts in Iran were formed by such an erosion process.

The erosion cycles that have taken place since the middle Pleistocene in Pakistan have been studied by Brinkman and Rafiq (1971). In the Sulaiman

and Kirthar ranges there are steep, nearly bare hill slopes. Between the hills are valleys and basins of varying sizes. The same conditions occur in major parts of Afghanistan, Iran and Iraq, especially in the arid and semiarid areas. The material eroded from the hills is deposited in the valleys as gravelly fans, gravelly and loamy piedmont plains, and clayey playas. The deposits range in age from the middle Pleistocene to recent. The middle Pleistocene deposits are generally tilted and the gravelly parts are somewhat consolidated. They were mostly eroded during the last interglacial period and their remnants are found as dissected terraces in the upper parts of the watersheds or along the hills. The valleys are now mostly covered by material deposited during the last glacial age or later. Considerable areas of mainly gravelly and some loamy terraces of the last glacial age occur in the upper parts of the valleys. They are somewhat dissected. The dissection probably began at the end of the last glaciation, when large-scale thawing occurred and permafrost conditions ended. The eroded material was deposited in the bottoms of the valleys and basins. This erosion process is continuous. Soil formation took place mainly during the early Holocene on older surfaces and continued during the middle Holocene. The younger deposits show very little soil formation.

Most of the valley deposits are silty and seem to be partly composed of loessial material. Some small enclosed basins in hill regions have typical loess deposits. The loess was probably deposited during the last glacial age and occupies many closed valleys. Due to later erosion it was transported by runoff, mixed with other materials and re-sorted by water. These findings will probably hold good for most mountain valleys in Afghanistan and arid and semi-arid areas of Iran.

In the lower Himalayas there are also valleys filled with loess of the last glacial age. The same loess covers the greater part of the Potwar upland around Rawalpindi, between the Himalayas and the Salt range. Older deposits of loess and alluvium are only exceptionally found under this recent loess deposit, as they were largely removed by extensive erosion during the last interglacial period. The recent loess has also been extensively dissected, probably toward the end of the last glaciation when large-scale thawing occurred.

The eroded loess material was transported to the Punjab plains and formed river terraces. Soil formation in the uneroded parts of the loess and the river terraces started during the early Holocene. The Himalayan valleys and the Potwar upland were stabilized by vegetation during the early Holocene, a period of higher rainfall than the present. A new erosion phase started owing to the decreased silt load in the rivers. Erosion became active on the terraces of the upper Indus plains (Punjab plains) while the area of the lower Indus plains was filled with new sediments. The Pleistocene river terraces which occupy extensive areas in the Ganges plain (Wadia, 1953) and the Euphrates plain (Buringh, 1960) probably have the same history.

In the Himalayas, especially in the southern part, the slopes are steep, and colluvial deposition, including slope creep, predominates. The upper parts of the slopes are generally bare or have only a thin cover of weathered material, but the lower parts have thick colluvial deposits. Owing to continuous erosion the surface is usually of recent age and only weak soil formation is noticed. However, some valleys, such as that of the Jhelum river, have Pleistocene river terraces (Wadia, 1953).

Although it has a long history of sand deposition, the Thar desert probably acquired its present form during the last glacial age, when the sand was built up into ridges which were stabilized by vegetation during the early Holocene, a period of higher rainfall than the present. However, the presence of caliche, a lime hardpan, and remnants of gypsic horizon in some interdunal valleys indicates that the dunes in some areas have existed since the middle Pleistocene.

References

BRINKMAN, R. & RAFIQ, M.   *Landforms and soil parent materials*
1971   *in West Pakistan*.   Lahore, Central Soil Research Institute, Pakistan. Soils Bulletin No. 2. FAO/UNDP Soil Survey Project, Pakistan.

BURINGH, P.   *Soils and soil conditions in Iraq*, p. 34-42. Baghdad,
1960   Ministry of Agriculture.

DEWAN, M.L. & FAMOURI, J.   *The soils of Iran*, p. 21-27.
1964   Rome, FAO. FAO and Soil Institute of Iran.

KING, L.C.   *The morphology of the earth*.   Edinburgh and
1962   London, Oliver and Boyd.

WADIA, D.N.   *Geology of India*. 3rd ed.   London, Macmil-
1953   lan.

GEOLOGY AND LITHOLOGY

Geologic history

The Indian and Arabian shields (Figure 4) are parts of Gondwanaland, one of the oldest land masses. They have a basement of Archaean rocks, probably formed by solidification of the earth's original crust. Gondwanaland was separated from the northern continent of Angaraland by the Tethys Sea. At the beginning of the Eocene Gondwanaland broke up and its parts drifted away to form Australia, Africa, the Arabian Peninsula and South America. A part of it remains at or near its original place, forming the Indian shield. The break-up of Gondwanaland took place in stages (Wadia, 1953).

At the end of the Cretaceous and during the early Eocene Gondwanaland (especially the Indian shield part) experienced a period of intense volcanic activity associated with deep-seated faulting. Several hundred thousand square kilometres of the continent were covered by basaltic lava. Lava deposits found on the Arabian shield are related to those on the Indian shield. It is believed that the mass of the lava — more than the bulk of the entire Himalaya mountains — probably upset the balance of the earth's crust, and set in motion the forces which broke up Gondwanaland and raised the bed of the Tethys Sea into mountain systems such as the Himalaya, Hindu Kush, Elburz and Zagros ranges.

During the Palaeozoic and Mesozoic the Tethys Sea extended over the area of the Himalayas, the Indo-Gangetic plain, Burma, Assam, Afghanistan, Iran and part of Iraq, and further west up to the Alps. The Caspian and Mediterranean seas are its remnants. The mountain-building processes which began in the Eocene are still active, as shown by frequent earthquakes. In the Himalayas three main periods of mountain-building activities have been recognized. They probably extended to other areas of the Tethys Sea as well. The first upheaval, which raised the central axis of the Himalayas, took place toward the end of the Eocene, shortly after the break-up of Gondwanaland. The second occurred during the middle Miocene and the third began at the end of the Pliocene and continued into the late Pleistocene. Some parts of the Himalayas were raised by 1 000 to 2 000 metres as recently as the late Pleistocene.

The probable periods of formation of the various closely related mountain ranges are given as follows:

Hindu Kush range.   The main uplift took place during the Miocene-Pliocene, part in the Eocene.

Kirthar range.   Miocene-Pliocene-Pleistocene.

Quetta axial belt (part of Kirthar range).   Eocene, contemporary to the first upheaval in the Himalayas.

Makran range (part of Kirthar range).   Oligocene-Pleistocene.

Zagros range.   The first phase started in the late Jurassic in the northeastern and southeastern parts, the second phase in the Eocene-Pliocene.

Oman mountains.   Related to the Zagros range.

Elburz range.   Mid-Miocene. Faulting and thrusting were accompanied by igneous intrusions in the Eocene and Oligocene. Compression occurred in the late Jurassic and late Cretaceous.

Iranian plateau. The main upheaval took place in the Pliocene. Igneous rocks formed in places during the late Cretaceous and Tertiary. There was much volcanic activity in the Eocene, less in the Oligocene and Miocene.

Northern Levant and southern Levant. Eocene.

The Indian shield experienced four periods of diastrophic earth movements before the Precambrian which caused a high degree of metamorphism in the old basement rocks. It has been a stable area ever since. The later movements, including the Eocene lava effusion, were connected with only vertical fractures. The same is true to some extent for the Arabian shield, which has been a stable land mass since the beginning of the Cambrian.

Geological regions

The description of the geology and lithology of South Asia is based on the three morphostructural regions discussed in the previous section on geomorphology:

A. *The Indian shield and the Indo-Gangetic plain.*

B. *The Arabian shield and the Median zone*, including the Arabian shield, the Median zone, the Mesopotamian plain and the Rub al-Khali.

C. *The Tethys geosyncline*, including the Burmese part of the Sunda platform.

These morphostructural regions are subdivided into 44 geological regions which are outlined below and are shown in Figure 4. The parent materials are shown in Figure 5.

A. Indian shield and Indo-Gangetic plain

    A.1   Archaean system
    A.2   Dharwar system
    A.3   Cuddapah and Vindhyan systems
    A.4   Gondwana system
    A.5   Deccan trap
    A.6   Alluvial and coastal deposits
    A.7   Indo-Gangetic plain
    A.8   Thar desert

B. Arabian shield and Median zone

    B.1   Arabian shield
    B.2   Yemen plateau
    B.3   Al-Tihamah plain
    B.4   Hadhramaut plateau
    B.5   Yemen plains
    B.6   Jiddat al-Harasis plain
    B.7   Rub al-Khali desert
    B.8   Jabal Tuwaiq region
    B.9   Al-Summan region

    B.10   Al-Nafud desert
    B.11   Al-Dibdibah region
    B.12   Al-Hijarah and Al-Hamad regions
    B.13   Al-Widyan plain
    B.14   Mesopotamian plain
    B.15   Al-Jazirah region
    B.16   Eastern Jordan plateau
    B.17   Al-Tubayq region
    B.18   Northern Levant
    B.19   Southern Levant and Sinai Peninsula
    B.20   Jebel al-Druz plateau

C. Tethys geosyncline

    C.1   Shan plateau
    C.2   Arakan Yoma range
    C.3   Irrawaddy basin
    C.4   Assam plateau
    C.5   Great Himalayas
    C.6   Kashmir Himalayas
    C.7   Siwalik system
    C.8   Eastern Baluchistan ranges
    C.9   Baluchistan axial belt
    C.10   Makran range
    C.11   Hindu Kush system
    C.12   Dasht-i-Margo and Dasht-i-Tahlab basins
    C.13   Zagros mountain system
    C.14   Elburz mountain system
    C.15   Central Iranian plateau
    C.16   Taftan region

A. INDIAN SHIELD AND INDO-GANGETIC PLAIN

The Indian shield covers all the area south of the Indo-Gangetic plain, forming a plateau with mesas and buttes. It has a general eastward trend. The two most important mountain ranges running along the coasts of India are the Western Ghats and the Eastern Ghats, which attain altitudes ranging from 900 to 1 500 metres. There are also some lower hill ranges (the Vindhya, Aravalli and Gondwana) which rise from 400 to 1 000 metres.

The shield area has had a stable basement since the Precambrian and has not been subject to extensive folding since then. However, vertical movements from beneath have caused block subsidence along nearly vertical faults, or effusion of lava through fractures. The various rock formations are as follows:

A1. *Archaean system*

The Indian shield basement consists of a complex of Archaean gneisses with plutonic intrusions. These rocks are exposed over more than half the area. They are extremely contorted and highly metamorphosed as a result of volcanic activity, folding and faulting. The most common Archaean rock is azoic gneiss with some schist, but in some places intrusive granite is also found. Orthoclase is the most predominant constituent of the rocks.

A2. *Dharwar system*

The Dharwar system is closely related to the Archaean gneisses and is probably of the same age. It is a complex of sedimentary and igneous rocks, all of which were highly metamorphosed to form schists and gneisses. They are hardly distinguishable from the Archaean gneisses and form a part of the shield basement. Very intense and extensive tectonic movements took place during the late Dharwar, folding the rocks into complicated wrinkles and creating a number of hill ranges (e.g. the Aravallis).

A3. *The Cuddapah and Vindhyan systems*

The Cuddapah system is composed of ancient sedimentary strata which overlie the Archaean and Dharwar complexes. The rocks are metamorphosed only locally, indicating a decrease in diastrophism in the shield area. The main rocks are compacted shale, slate, quartzite, siliceous hornstone and limestone.

The Vindhyan system is a practically undisturbed formation developed mainly in the Vindhya hills. The lower formation consists of marine shale, limestone and sandstone, and the upper part comprises fluviatile and estuarine sandstones. Metamorphism associated with some folding is noticed only in the southern Aravalli hills. At the end of the Vindhyan era all orogenic movements ceased in the peninsular area.

A4. *Gondwana system*

This system forms one vast, conformable sequence of upper Carboniferous to upper Jurassic fluviatile and lacustrine deposits laid down in great troughs which were formed by block subsidence associated with deep, nearly vertical fractures. Two extensive belts of the Gondwana outcrops occur along the Godavari and Mahanadi rivers, and a number of scattered outcrops are found in the Bengal region. The lower system consists of sandstone and shale intruded by coal seams, whereas the upper system is composed of massive sandstone, shale, coal seams and limestone. In the Bengal region the rocks are intrusive igneous.

A5. *Deccan trap*

The Deccan trap consists of vast, thick lava beds. Toward the end of the Cretaceous and in the early Eocene, lava poured from deep fissures in the earth's crust and covered the land, obliterating all existing topography and creating an immense volcanic plateau.

The thick lava beds are separated by thin, discontinuous sedimentary strata. The rock is singularly uniform augite basalt.

A6. *Alluvial and coastal deposits*

The Narmada and Tapti troughs in the Deccan trap are tectonic depressions filled with a 150-metre-thick alluvium of reddish yellow clay intercalated with sand and gravel. Along the east coast there is a continuous belt of coastal deposits. On the west coast they include the lowland of Gujarat, the Rann of Kutch and a very narrow coastal belt. The coastal deposits consist of fluviatile, deltaic and lagoon sediments which are often overlain by aeolian sands.

A7. *Indo-Gangetic plain*

The Indo-Gangetic plain occupies a vast geosyncline between the Himalayan ranges and the Indian shield. It was filled with eroded material during the orogenesis of the Himalayas. Some geologists calculate the depth of the geosyncline at its northern end to be about 5 000 metres. This depth decreases gradually toward the south. The plain is bounded on the north by a major fault at the foot of the Himalayas.

The surface of the plain is composed of Pleistocene and recent alluvium. The Pleistocene alluvium occurs mainly as piedmont deposits along the Himalayan foothills and as old river terraces. In Pakistan these Pleistocene deposits extend up to Multan in the south, and contain loess deposits in the Rawalpindi and Peshawar areas. In Bangladesh they occupy a piedmont strip in the north and remnants of old river terraces in the central region. In India they extend over a considerable part of the Ganges plain. The remaining area is covered by recent alluvium. The alluvium is calcareous and mainly silty or loamy. Only in the lower Indus plains and the Ganges delta is it clayey. The lower layers consist of massive clay and sand beds. However, the Brahmaputra deposits are noncalcareous.

The Thal plain between the Indus and Jhelum rivers is a sandy, wind-modified Pleistocene river terrace. The sand is calcareous and consists mostly of quartz with feldspar admixtures.

A8. *Thar desert*

The Thar desert is a vast expanse of thick Pleistocene sand deposits with a few outcrops of the old basement rocks. There are 10- to 30-metre-high sand ridges and dunes of various shapes. The area was relatively stable during the late Tertiary and Pleistocene, but the calcareous sand deposits date mainly from the Pleistocene.

B. ARABIAN SHIELD AND MEDIAN ZONE

The Arabian shield covers the western quarter of this area, the major part of which comprises the Median zone, where Cretaceous and Tertiary sedimentary deposits overlie the shield basement. In the northeast is a geosyncline comprising the Mesopotamian plain. The various subregions are as follows:

B1. *Arabian shield*

This shield has been a stable land area since the Cambrian. It includes the major part of the Najd plateau, all of the Hijaz, and part of the Asir mountains. Before the Cambrian this area was subjected to several phases of downwarping, folding, thrusting, sedimentation and erosion. In the Eocene a large part of it was covered by a thick deposit of basaltic lava which effused through vertical fissures. The lava here is comparable to that in the Deccan trap in India.

The Arabian shield consists of metamorphic, intrusive and effusive rocks. The metamorphic rocks are Precambrian and consist of gneiss, quartzite, phyllite, chert, marble and slate. The intrusive rocks are of Precambrian to Palaeozoic age and consist mainly of granite, gneiss, rhyolite, trachyte, syenite, diorite and some ultrabasic rocks. The effusives, mainly Tertiary and Quaternary, consist of olivine-rich titaniferous basalt, rhyolite and trachyte.

B2. *Yemen plateau*

This is a relatively high plateau formed on the Precambrian basement. In the Yemen Arab Republic the basement is partly covered by horizontal strata of Jurassic, Cretaceous and Tertiary sedimentary rocks. In addition to the sedimentaries there are massive extrusives (basalt, rhyolite and andesite) of late Cretaceous to recent age in the Yemen Arab Republic and the southwestern part of the People's Democratic Republic of Yemen. In the Aden area gently folded Mesozoic and Tertiary formations occur.

The Precambrian rocks consist of dominant granite, gneiss and schist, and subordinate quartzite, syenite, chert and crystalline limestone.

B3. *Al-Tihamah plain*

The Al-Tihamah coastal plain, a sediment-filled part of the Red Sea graben, slopes gently to the Red Sea. It is composed of Tertiary and Quaternary marine sediments covered by recent aeolian and alluvial deposits of sand, silt and gravel. Coral deposits are found below a 3-metre terrace.

B4. *Hadhramaut plateau*

This dissected high plateau has a northward tilt. The southern part is a tableland of Palaeocene limestone capped by Eocene mesas and cuestas and cut by an intricate drainage network. In the north it is separated from the plains to the west by an escarpment, and has a gentle eastward tilt.

The plateau consists mainly of Tertiary rocks: calcareous shale, limestone and some marl in the west, and massive gypsum with chert and marly bands interbedded with limestone in the east. Near the Gulf of Aden there are Cretaceous sandstone and siltsone with some shale and marl.

B5. *Yemen plains*

These two plains are composed mainly of gravel and sand, and are separated by a desert. Low hills and mesas of Cretaceous rocks occur sporadically. There are extensive gravel and scree terraces in the north. The Archaean basement rocks outcrop in the west.

The desert decreases in width from southwest to northeast, so that in the Wadi Hadhramaut only isolated patches of sand are found. There are long sand ridges which rise to 50 metres, two salt domes and some Archaean basement outcrops.

B6. *Jiddat al-Harasis plain*

This flat gravel plain is dotted with low eroded ridges and scree hills of Eocene age. There are also some mobile sand dunes. In the eastern part the gravel overlies chalk and marl, which are underlain by Cretaceous limestone. In the southwest and the north the underlying rock is fine-grained hard limestone.

B7. *Rub al-Khali desert*

This vast area of gravel plains and sand deserts lies in the southern part of the Arabian Peninsula. The sand is mainly aeolian and occurs as very high, long ridges, many of which are up to 150 metres high and exceed 40 km in length. Their trend is east-northeast.

B8. *Jabal Tuwaiq region*

This region and Al-Summan form the interior platform of the Arabian Peninsula. Jabal Tuwaiq has a gentle eastward slope. Before the upheaval it formed a depression where 5 500-metre-thick sediments of Cambrian to Pliocene age accumulated on the Arabian shield basement. On the west it is separated from the Arabian shield by a fault scarp running in a curve known as the Central Arabian Arc. The main rocks in the western part are silicified limestone and compact limestone of shallow water origin. In the central part there are sandstone and soft marly limestone. In the east there is a 70-km-wide strip of aeolian sand.

B9. *Al-Summan region*

Al-Summan is a remarkably flat area on the interior platform of the Arabian Peninsula where the eastward slope of the crystalline basement no longer prevails. Some parts have gentle undulations, possibly related to a horst and graben system at great depth. Others show major anticlinal north-south trends. The predominant rocks are marly sandstone, sandy marl and sandy limestone, mostly covered by limestone gravel. Near the Persian Gulf Miocene sandstone is exposed.

B10. *Al-Nafud desert*

Al-Nafud is a vast area of aeolian sand which is generally loose and forms dunes aligned in many different directions. There are many tilted sandstone outcrops.

B11. *Al-Dibdibah region*

Al-Dibdibah is largely a flat area with some low elongated hills. Structurally it forms the northeastern boundary of the interior platform discussed under B8 and B9. The surface is covered with gravel consisting of pebbles of various igneous rocks, quartz and gritstone. In some places there is aeolian sand.

B12. *Al-Hijarah and Al-Hamad regions*

Al-Hijarah is a flat Tertiary limestone desert lying to the west of the Mesopotamian plain. The topography is controlled by a series of fault scarps running roughly north-south.

The northwestern part of the Al-Hamad region is a featureless plain, and the southern part consists of endless stretches of gravelly and stony land, and sand dunes. In the north there is a limestone steppe with several basalt plateaus.

The Tertiary deposits overlying the Arabian shield are very thick and consist mainly of limestone and dolomite interbedded with marl, and shale, chert and siliceous dolomite. In the Al-Hamad the main rocks are Eocene limestone and chalk overlain by sandy limestone, marl and clay.

B13. *Al-Widyan plain*

Al-Widyan is a nearly flat plain with a gentle eastern slope. It is an extension of the interior platform of the Arabian Peninsula where thick horizontal beds of Cretaceous and Tertiary sedimentary rocks overlie the Archaean basement of the Arabian shield. Deep wadis have been formed by erosion. The main rocks are limestone, chalky limestone, dolomite, dolomitic and shaly marl and shale, with some massive or crossbedded sandstone.

B14. *Mesopotamian plain*

This plain forms the southern part of a geosyncline filled in with old shelf sediments and later deposits. The upper part consists of very young river sediments and some irrigation sediments (Buringh, 1960). Most alluvial sediments are erosional products of the mountains to the north and east. Some material has come also from the deserts to the west.

The surface of the plain consists of Pleistocene and recent alluvial deposits. The Pleistocene deposits occur as old alluvial terraces in the north. The high terraces consist of sandy, loamy and silty materials mixed with gravel. Quite often the surface has a desert pavement or a salt crust. The lower terraces and flood plains have layers of silt, loam and clay interbedded with thin sand layers. The alluvium has mixed mineralogy, is calcareous and contains gypsum.

The lower delta area consists of mudflats, but north of it is an extensive area of swamps which is probably a depression formed by a very recent crustal subsidence (Lees and Falcon, 1952).

B15. *Al-Jazirah region*

Al-Jazirah forms part of the geosyncline in which the Mesopotamian plain occurs. It consists of an undulating low plateau with a number of small closed basins. The largest basin, the Wadi Tharthar, may be a tectonic depression. Some low hills are extensions of the Zagros mountains.

The western part consists of Miocene gypsum and anhydrite deposits interbedded with green marls. Sandstone, clay and sandy clay are found in the east.

B16. *Eastern Jordan plateau*

The plateau is a peneplain consisting of Cretaceous and Eocene marine sediments. In the east the sedimentary strata are nearly horizontal, showing differential block uplift. Toward the western edge the influence of scarp rifting is quite pronounced. The plateau consists of Eocene chalk, cherty and nummulitic limestone, and marl. Crystalline limestone and marble also occur. In the south gravel and sand overlie the limestone.

B17. *Al-Tubayq region*

Al-Tubayq is a sandstone plain mainly covered with loose sand or mudflats. The main rocks are crossbedded sandstone, shaly sandstone and shale. In the east there is sandstone with common quartz pebbles. In the northeast there is a gravel plain.

B18. *Northern Levant*

The northern Levant comprises the Jabal Ansariye, the Lebanon range, the Galilee upland and the Anti-Lebanon range including Mount Hermon.

Jabal Ansariye consists of a broad, gently folded anticline flanked by Jurassic limestone and sandstone. The average elevation is 1 200 metres. Fracturing is pronounced in the north. The most important fault is the Ghab, occupied by the Orontes river. Separated from the Jabal Ansariye by a tectonic depression known as the Tripoli-Homs gap is the Lebanon range, which consists of a single upfold intersected by numerous faults, along some of which basalt has extruded. The Galilee upland, an extension of the Lebanon range, consists of low rounded hills and grass-covered undulating plains with an average elevation of 500 metres. The Anti-Lebanon range, a prototype of the Levant system, essentially consists of a simple anticlinal structure with a southwest-northeast trend. Mount Hermon in the south is an extension of the Anti-Lebanon anticline.

The greater part of the northern Levant consists of Cretaceous and Jurassic compact limestone and dolomitic limestone that are sometimes intercalated with nummulitic sands and clays. The Tripoli-Homs gap is mainly covered by basalt. The Al-Biqa valley between the Lebanon and Anti-Lebanon ranges is filled with Quaternary alluvium. The base and lower slopes of Mount Hermon have basalt overlying Cretaceous limestone.

B19. *Southern Levant and Sinai Peninsula*

In the southern Levant the thickness of the sedimentary deposits (mainly Cretaceous limestone and marl) on the Archaean basement decreases from north to south, so that the basement appears at the surface in the southern part of the Sinai Peninsula. The southern Levant and the peninsula are bounded on the east by a tectonic rift running from the Gulf of Aqaba to the Dead Sea, and from there north along the Jordan rift valley.

In the north is the Judea plateau, separated from the Negev plateau by an east-west-running fault. In the Negev plateau the Archaean basement is quite close to the surface. In the south the Sinai plateau is tilted to the north and drops to sea level in the southwest along a series of step faults.

B20. *Jebel al-Druz plateau*

This area is a basalt plateau where many types of volcanic products (ash, scoria and granite) are found in addition to sheets of basalt. The basalt sheets are intercalated with sedimentary deposits. The maximum volcanic activity probably occurred during the Pliocene, although eruptions also occurred in the Quaternary.

C. TETHYS GEOSYNCLINE

Extending from the Alps to the Himalayas and beyond, this area is characterized by close folding and strong thrusting, largely directed from the north. The upheavals started in the Eocene, continued in phases during the Tertiary and extended into the Pleistocene. Some areas, such as the Zagros mountain region, were affected by upheavals in the Jurassic. Some stages of folding and uplifting were accompanied by deep-seated faulting which brought lava to the surface. Although the Shan plateau does not form part of the Tethyan area, it has undergone Tertiary orogenesis, and will be discussed here.

C1. *Shan plateau*

Geotectonically, this highland is the western limit of the Sunda platform, which is mainly a stable land mass. Its geological structure is relatively simple; the hill ranges are mainly anticlines and the valleys synclines.

The major part of the area has marine deposits of Precambrian to Jurassic age (slate, quartzite, shale and limestone) overlain by Oligocene and Miocene deposits (shale and clay). Old lake basins have upper Tertiary and Pleistocene sediments. Archaean gneiss is exposed in the west. Granite occupies a considerable area in the east.

C2. *Arakan Yoma range*

This mountain range, with peaks rising to 2 500 metres above sea level, is formed by a series of fold structures, with open regular folding. The old crystalline rocks which constitute the core are flanked by hard, tightly folded, mainly Tertiary rocks. The dominant rocks are Tertiary shale, sandstone and limestone and Cretaceous-Eocene metamorphosed sandstone and shale. Intrusive granite occurs in the northeast.

C3. *Irrawaddy basin*

This Tertiary geosynclinal basin was successively filled with fluviatile, estuarine, and brackish water, and marine sediments. A great fault separates it from the Shan plateau, and a monoclinal fold forms its western boundary. The main rocks are shale, sandstone and young alluvium. In the north there are some areas of metamorphic gneiss as well as basalt and granite.

C4. *Assam plateau*

As it has almost escaped the Tertiary folding, this plateau may be considered part of the Indian shield. There is a slight tilt to the northeast. The average altitude is about 1 000 metres. The main rocks are Archaean gneiss and granite and Precambrian quartzite, slate and schist.

The Himalayan ranges

The Himalayas can be divided into three broad geological zones: the northern or Tibetan zone north of the main mountain ranges, which lies outside the region covered by the Soil Map of South Asia and is not discussed; the central or Great Himalayas (C5) and the Kashmir Himalayas (C6); and the Siwalik system (C7).

C5. *Great Himalayas*

The Great Himalayas, comprising several parallel or converging mountain ranges, are mainly composed of crystalline and metamorphic rocks, with unfossiliferous sediments of Precambrian and Cambrian age. Uplifted in three stages, they consist of a series of anticlines, with intense folding and faulting caused by thrusts from the north. The southern faces of the anticlines are often faulted. Along some thrust plains in the central part of the Himalayas the older rocks have been uplifted and folded over the younger ones. Their average elevation is about 6 000 metres and they have the world's highest peaks (Mount Everest, Mount Kanchenjunga and others). The southern slopes are generally steep and the northern slopes relatively gentle.

The bulk of the Himalayan high ranges consists of crystalline or metamorphic rocks (granite, granulite, phyllite and schist) which are partly considered as Archaean gneiss and partly as much younger gneiss of intrusive origin. Other main rocks are slate, limestone and sandstone. In the late Cretaceous and early Eocene, igneous, intrusive and extrusive rocks, granite, gabbro, peridotite, rhyolite, andesite and basalt covered large areas in the northwest. The outer flanks of the central core have Eocene gypseous shale and limestone, and Miocene brackish water clay and lacustrine sandstone.

C6. *Kashmir Himalayas*

The central Himalayan axis has two western branches: the northern one runs to the northwest

as the Zaskar range, and the southern one runs west as the Dhauladhar and Pir Panjal ranges. These mountain ranges are about 4 000 to 6 000 metres high and are cut by deep ravines. Between these two branches of the crystalline axis lies the synclinal Kashmir valley.

Archaean gneiss and schist occur with Precambrian and Cambrian slate and phyllite intercalated with limestone and quarzite. Limestone, shale, slate and dolomite also occur. Pleistocene deposits occupy nearly half of the Kashmir valley.

C7. *Siwalik system*

This system is a belt of foothills along the Himalayas and the Sulaiman range. The fluviatile Mio-Pleistocene deposits of sand, clay and gravel were folded and uplifted during the last phase (Plio-Pleistocene) of the Himalayan upheaval. The contact of the Siwaliks with the older Tertiary system is formed by the main boundary fault, which is reversed and has an apparent throw of thousands of metres. The structure of the Siwaliks is a simple succession of broad anticlines and synclines. The rocks are mainly sandstone, clay and conglomerate.

C8. *Eastern Baluchistan ranges*

This system, formed of lower Tertiary to Pleistocene deposits, includes the Kirthar, Brahui and Sulaiman ranges. The Kirthar mountains consist of anticlines forming hogback relief with 300- to 1 000-metre-high scarps of a north-south trend. The east Sulaiman range, which is about 2 000 metres high, runs north-south but swings westward south of 30°N to join the Kirthar range. The main rock is limestone, with subordinate shales, sandstone and conglomerates. The rocks are of Eocene and Mio-Pliocene age.

C9. *Baluchistan axial belt*

This belt comprises long narrow ridges consisting of a succession of normal anticlinal hills and synclinal valleys. The oldest rocks, exposed near Quetta, are Triassic shale and slate which rest unconformably on Permo-Carboniferous limestone. However, the main rocks are Cretaceous and Jurassic limestone.

C10. *Makran range*

The Makran range is a series of echeloned ridges occurring in an arc and extending from the Zagros mountains in the southwest to Quetta in the northeast. The mountains, mainly of a simple anticlinal structure, are developed in relatively soft Tertiary sandstone, shale and mudstone with a flysch facies in the north.

C11. *Hindu Kush system*

The Hindu Kush system consists of two west-east-running parallel ranges. The central Hindu Kush range merges with the Paropamisus range in the north and the Koh-i-Baba and Band-i-Baian ranges in the south. The highest parts of the Hindu Kush ranges have Precambrian crystalline rocks flanked by metamorphic Palaeozoic rocks which cover extensive areas. Other rocks are limestone, sandstone, marl and clay of Tertiary age.

C12. *Dasht-i-Margo and Dasht-i-Tahlab basins*

These synclinal basins between the Hindu Kush and the Makran range have been filled in with material eroded from the surrounding mountains. The deposits are mainly silt, clay and aeolian sand. The dry lakes occupying the lowest parts are covered with salt.

C13. *Zagros mountain system*

This mountain system consists of a number of almost parallel, northwest-southeast-aligned ranges which are about 3 000 metres high. The main rock is massive limestone formed during the Palaeozoic, Mesozoic and Eocene. Large deposits of Eocene gypsum and salt occur, and schist, gneiss, slate and granite are also found. Folding and faulting occurred in several periods, starting in the late Jurassic in the northeast and in the upper Cretaceous in the southeast. During the Eocene-Pliocene period the whole area was affected by earth movements. In the north, differential tectonic movements along well-marked faults formed horst blocks and downthrow basins. Numerous volcanic cones indicate recurrent volcanic activity. In the south, folding with nearly parallel anticlines and synclines is the main feature. The Oman mountains, comprising the Al-Hajar al-Gharbi, Jabal Akhdar and Al-Hajar al-Sharki ranges, are structurally a part of the Zagros mountain system and consist of an upfold of Cretaceous rocks with a Precambrian core. The main rocks are chert, limestone, gabbro, diorite and some other ultrabasic rocks.

C14. *Elburz mountain system*

From the upper Jurassic to the middle Miocene, material continuously accumulated in this part of the Tethys geosyncline. The upheaval, accompanied by igneous intrusions, probably took place in the late Miocene. Some compression dates back to the late Cretaceous. The mountain core consists of Jurassic and Cretaceous sediments, with Palaeocene formations along the flanks. The main rock is limestone. Tuff beds along with volcanic and intrusive rocks occur in the south. Schist and other metamorphic rocks cover an extensive area in the northwest. Loess occurs in the north and southeast.

C15. *Central Iranian plateau*

This plateau consists of a series of closed basins and low mountains of Oligo-Miocene rocks. The mountains encircle a central depression. During the late Tertiary and Quaternary the basins were occupied by lakes. The surfaces of these basins are covered with sand and silt. A salt crust is found in the central depression. There are also some extensive areas of sand dunes.

A great line of faults separates the central Iranian plateau from the Zagros mountains. Extrusive rocks such as basalt, tuff and andesite are found along this line as a result of the volcanic activity which developed fully in the Eocene but decreased in the Oligo-Miocene. In the mountains limestone occurs with some sandstone and shale. Gypsum, clay and mudstone occur in the north.

C16. *Taftan region*

This region is a broken, irregular highland. Structurally, its southern part is a continuation of the Makran range. Its northern part consists of Eocene volcanic rocks (tuff, diorite, andesite and others). There is a great volcanic complex of basaltic rocks associated with partly active cones of the Taftan group. In the south granite, diorite, schist and sandstone are found.

References

MAPS

Geological map of Asia and the Far East, 1:5 000 000. U.N. 1961 Economic Commission for Asia and the Far East.

Geological map of India, 1 : 6 111 100. 1940

National Atlas of India, 1 : 5 000 000. 1957

Geological map of Ceylon, 1 : 1 175 000. (After Fernando).

Geological map of Burma, 1 : 2 000 000. Burma Geological Department.

Geological map of Pakistan, 1 : 2 000 000. Geological Survey 1964 of Pakistan.

Geological map of Iran, 1 : 2 500 000. National Iranian Oil 1957 Company.

Carte géologique du Moyen-Orient par L. Dubertret. Echelle 1942 1 : 2 000 000.

Carte lithologique de la bordure orientale de la Méditerranée 1942 par L. Dubertret. Echelle 1 : 500 000.

Carte lithologique de la Syrie et du Liban par L. Dubertet. Echelle 1944 1 : 1 000 000.

Generalized lithological map of the Khuzistan's river basins,
1955 1 : 2 000 000. National Iranian Oil Company.

Geological map of Israel by I.L. Picard. Scale 1 : 5 000 000.
1959

Geological map of Jordan, 1 : 250 000.
1956

Geological map of the Arabian Peninsula, 1 : 2 000 000. U.S.
1963 Geological Survey and the Arabian-American Oil
Company.

PUBLICATIONS

ALTAIE, F.H. *The soils of Iraq.* p. 5-10. Ghent, State Univer-
1968 sity of Ghent. (Thesis) (Mimeographed)

ARAMCO. *ARAMCO Handbook.* New York, Arabian-Amer-
1960 ican Oil Company.

ATKINSON, K. *et al. Soil conservation survey of Wadi Shueib*
1967 *and Wadi Kufrein, Jordan,* p. 5-8. Durham, University
of Durham; Amman, National Resources Authority.

BRINKMAN, R. & RAFIQ, M. *Landforms and soil parent ma-*
1971 *terials in West Pakistan,* p. 28. Pakistan Soils Bulletin
No. 2, FAO/UNDP Soil Survey Project, Pakistan. Lahore,
Central Soil Research Institute.

BURDON, D.J. *Handbook of the geology of Jordan.* Colchester,
1959 Benham.

BURINGH, P. *Soils and soil conditions in Iraq.* Baghdad,
1960 Ministry of Agriculture.

DE VAUMAS, E. *Le Liban. Etude de géographie physique.*
1954 *Parties 1, 2 et 3.* Paris, Firmin-Didot.

DEWAN, M.L. & FAMOURI, J. *The soils of Iran,* p. 21-27.
1964 Rome, FAO. FAO and Soil Institute of Iran.

DUBERTRET, L. *Géologie du site de Beyrouth.* Beyrouth,
1945 Délégation générale de France au Levant. Section
Géologie.

ERGUN, H.N. *Report to the Government of Kuwait on recon-*
1969 *naissance soil survey,* p. 5-10. Rome. (FAO/KU/TF 17).

FALCON, N.L. The geology of the northeast margin of the
1967 Arabian basement shield. *Advancement of Science,*
24(119): 11.

FAO. *Report to the Government of Saudi Arabia on recon-*
1953 *naissance soil and land classification of the south Asir*
Tihama, p. 3-6. Rome. FAO/EPTA Report No. 69.

FAO. *FAO Mediterranean development project, Lebanon*
1959 *Country Report,* 2: 1-3. Rome.

FAO. *Soil survey report of the Hussainiyah Beni Hassan drain-*
1960 *age project,* p. 10-11. Rome. FAO Publication No.
2075.

FAO. *Report to the Government of Saudi Arabia on future*
1963 *prospects for hydro-agricultural development,* p. 4-6.
Rome. FAO/EPTA Report No. 1638.

FAO. *Etude des ressources en eaux souterraines de la Jezireh*
1966 *syrienne,* p. 17-23. Rome. FAO/FS:17/SYR.

FAO. *Enquête pédologique et programmes d'irrigation connexes*
1969 *au Liban. Rapport final,* p. 7-12. Vol. 2, *Pédologie.*
FAO/PNUD.

FISHER, W.B. *The Middle East, a physical, social and regional*
1961 *geography. 4th ed.* London, Methuen.

FISHER, W.B. *et al. Soil survey of Wadi Ziqlab,* p. 4-12. Durham,
1966 University of Durham. Amman, National Resources
Authority.

HAGEN, T. *Nepal, the Kingdom in the Himalayas.* Berne,
1961 Kümmerly and Frey.

HUMLUM, J. *La géographie de l'Afghanistan.* Copenhague,
1959 Gyldendal.

HUNTING SURVEY CORPORATION. *Reconnaissance geology of*
1960 *part of West Pakistan,* p. 14-60. Government of Canada.

INDIA. MINISTRY OF EDUCATION AND SCIENTIFIC RESEARCH.
1957 *National Atlas of India.* New Delhi.

IRAN. NATIONAL IRANIAN OIL COMPANY. *Explanatory text*
1959 *to the geological map of Iran,* p. 18. Tehran.

ITALCONSULT. *Land and water surveys on the Wadi Jizan,*
1965 Vol. 5. Rome. United Nations Special Fund Project.

ITALCONSULT. *Water and agricultural surveys for areas II*
1969 *and III.* Rome. Report by Italconsult for the Kingdom
of Saudi Arabia.

KARAN, P.P. *Nepal. A cultural and physical geography,*
1960 p. 100. Lexington, University of Kentucky Press.

KING, L.C. *The morphology of the earth.* Edinburgh and
1962 London, Oliver and Boyd.

LAMARE, P. *Structure géologique de l'Arabie.*

LEBANON. INSTITUT DE RECHERCHES AGRONOMIQUES. *Notice*
1960 *explicative pour la carte d'utilisation des sols de la région*
El Hermel-El Kaa, p. 6-10. Tell Amara, Rayak.

LEES, G.M. & FALCON, N.L. The geographical history of
1952 the Mesopotamian plains. *Geogr. J.,* Vol. 68, Part 1.

QUENNELL, A.M. The structural and geomorphic evolution
1958 of the Dead Sea rift. *The Quarterly Journal of the*
Geological Society of London, Vol. 114.

SHAMOOT, S.A. & HUSSINI, K. *Land and water use in the*
1969 *Hashemite Kingdom of Jordan, Part I, Land Resources,*
p. 4-10. A paper submitted to the Near East Land and
Water Use Meeting held in Amman, Jordan, in May
1969. Amman, Al Hurieh.

STREBEL, O. Bodengesellschaften Syriens und des Libanons.
1965 *Geol. Jb.* No. 84.

TWITCHELL, K.S. *Saudi Arabia.* New Jersey, Princeton
1953 University Press.

UNECFA. *Explanatory text to the geological map of Asia and*
1961 *the Far East.* United Nations Economic Commission
for Asia and the Far East.

UNITED KINGDOM. ADMIRALTY. Syria. *Geographical hand-*
1943 *book series.* London, H.M.S.O.

WADIA, D.N. *Geology of India. 3rd ed.* London, Macmil-
1953 lan.

WILLIMOT, S.G. *et al. The Wadi El Hassa survey,* p. 4-10.
1963 Durham, University of Durham; Amman, National
Resources Authority.

WILLIMOT, S.G. *et al. Conservation survey of the southern*
1964 *highlands of Jordan,* p. 16-27. Durham, University of
Durham; Amman, National Resources Authority.

5. THE SOILS OF SOUTH ASIA

The legend of the Soil Map of South Asia consists of 408 map units in 350 different soil associations, each of which is composed of one or more soils occupying characteristic positions in the landscape. The sequence of their occurrence is related mainly to topography, geomorphology and lithology.

Each soil association is characterized by the dominant soil — the soil occupying the largest area in the map unit — and by associated soils and inclusions which occur in lesser proportion. Seventy-eight different dominant soils have been indicated on the map.

For convenience and brevity the soil associations have been listed in Table 4 with the following information:

1. The map symbol of the dominant soil, followed by the number specifying the composition of the soil association, a second number indicating the textural class of the dominant soil, and a small letter indicating the slope class of the soil association. Textural class numbers are: (1) coarse, (2) medium, (3) fine. Slope class letters are (a) level to undulating, (b) rolling to hilly, (c) steeply dissected to mountainous.

2. The associated soils — subdominant soils which cover more than 20% of the map unit.

3. Inclusions of important soils occupying less than 20% of the map unit.

4. Phases related to the presence of indurated layers, hard rock, or of salinity or alkalinity in the soil.

5. An estimate of the area of the unit in thousands of hectares.

6. The climate symbols.[1]

7. Countries of occurrence.

Distribution of major soils

The environmental conditions in South Asia are enormously varied. This applies to climate, vegetation, geomorphology, geology and lithology, and consequently to soils.

To aid in understanding the soil geography of South Asia, the subcontinent has been divided into nineteen soil regions, each with its own distribution of soils and peculiarities of land use (Figure 6). Starting from the Mediterranean coast in the west, each of these regions is described in terms of climate, natural vegetation, main rocks, and distribution of the main soils.

1. Xerosol-Luvisol association of the Fertile Crescent.

Extending from northeastern Iraq through northern and western Syria to northern Israel and western Jordan, this region is known as the Fertile Crescent of the Near East. It has been under cultivation since ancient times because the rainfall is sufficient for crops and fruit orchards. Elevations range from 500 to 3 000 metres.

The rocks are mainly Cretaceous or Tertiary limestone and marl with some nummulitic clays and sands. In some places basalt occurs. In the east Miocene gypsum and other anhydrite deposits are found interbedded with marl. Most of the soils are formed in Pleistocene alluvium derived from these rocks.

The main soils of this region are Calcic Xerosols, but Chromic Vertisols and Chromic Luvisols, each covering about 20% of the area, are also important. The Xerosols occur in a semiarid climate with 300 to 500 mm rainfall. They are stony in places, as in the western parts of Syria and Jordan. In northwestern Syria they are underlain by a petrocalcic horizon and in northeastern Iraq they are shallow over rock. The Chromic Vertisols occur in northern Iraq, northeastern and southwestern Syria, central Lebanon and some parts of Israel. These soils occupy concave valleys in the Xerosol area. The Luvisols are quite old and occur in areas near the Mediterranean coast where the rainfall is higher (500 to 900 mm). In some places they may even contain free lime. This has been attributed by van Liere (1965) to the deposition of dust from vast desert areas of calcareous soils. Some areas of

---

[1] According to the Papadakis system. See J. Papadakis, *Climates of the world and their agricultural potentialities*, Buenos Aires, 1966.

Calcaric Cambisols are associated with Luvisols, especially in southern Lebanon. They are developed from limestone. Lithosols occur on steep mountain slopes.

2. *Yermosol-Solonchak association of the Al-Tihamah coastal plain*

Extending in a narrow belt along the west coast of the Arabian Peninsula, the Al-Tihamah plain is formed by Quaternary alluvial deposits derived from the adjacent mountain ranges and the loessial material of the mountain valleys. The alluvium consists of 1- to 9-metre-thick loess-like silty material underlain by gravel. There are gravel deposits in some places and desert sand in others. The plain has a gentle slope from east to west, with elevations ranging between 0 and 300 metres (TESCO/FAO, 1971). The rainfall varies from 100 mm near the coast to 300 mm near the hills.

The dominant soils are Haplic Yermosols with a narrow strip of Gleyic Solonchaks along the coast. The northern part has mainly Orthic Solonchaks formed in areas which have been influenced by sea water flooding in the past. The Yermosols are formed in Pleistocene loess-like silty material or gravelly and loamy alluvium (Smith, 1970). They are slightly to moderately calcareous and have some lime specks in the B horizon. Scattered areas of Eutric or Calcaric Fluvisols occur on young alluvial deposits throughout the plain. They are mainly silty or loamy and are slightly or moderately calcareous.

3. *Yermosols of the Najd plateau*

This is a plain covering part of the Najd plateau in central Saudi Arabia where annual rainfall is about 100 mm. The soils are mainly loamy Haplic Yermosols which have developed in alluvium derived from the basalt and metamorphic rocks of the surrounding higher land. The Yermosols, mainly yellowish or gravelly loams, are developed in loamy, sandy and gravelly alluvium of Pleistocene age. The soil development probably took place in the Pleistocene or early Holocene under a higher rainfall than the present. There are some areas of Fluvisols on young alluvial deposits. Scattered Lithosols and rock outcrops occur in the area.

4. *Lithosol-Yermosol association of the Near Eastern plateaus and plains*

Covering major parts of the Arabian Peninsula, Iraq, Syria, Jordan and Israel, this is one of the most extensive soil regions. It is subdivided into two subregions: the shield area (4a) with mainly Cretaceous-

Eocene basalt and Precambrian plutonic and metamorphic rocks, and the area of sedimentary rocks (4b), with Tertiary limestone, marl and anhydrites as well as Pleistocene alluvium. Most of the region has an elevation of less than 1 000 metres, about one third is between 1 000 and 2 000 metres, and some mountains (the Asir and the Hijaz) rise to over 3 000 metres above sea level. The climate is hot and arid; rainfall is less than 100 mm over a major part of the region. A few areas in the north and southwest receive up to 250 mm annually.

Dominant soils are Lithosols on mountains and rock outcrops and Yermosols on peneplains and Pleistocene alluvial terraces. The Yermosols are mostly shallow, stony, or both, but in some spots they are deep, yellowish loams — the soil of oases. In the north they are intergrades to Xerosols. In northwestern Iraq, eastern Syria, Kuwait and the southern part of the Arabian Peninsula they are underlain by a petrogypsic horizon. In an area southeast of the Rub al-Khali desert they are underlain by a petrocalcic horizon. Some Solonchaks occur in basins and along the coast of the Persian Gulf. In the mountains in the southwest there are nearly level or gently undulating plains with deep silty or loamy Yermosols developed in Pleistocene loess-like deposits and loamy piedmont alluvium (Smith, 1970). The piedmont deposits occur in higher parts of the intermontane valleys or on alluvial fans at the foot of mountains. The silty soils are yellowish brown while the loamy soils are reddish brown or dark brown. As the temperatures are rather low owing to high altitudes (1 000 to 3 000 metres), the soils have a fair amount of organic matter. The western and southern slopes of the mountains with 400 to 1 000 mm rainfall have mainly yellowish brown moderately calcareous silty soils which may qualify as Xerosols, and there may be some Cambisols as well. The area west of the Al-Hajar mountains is an outwash plain on which gravelly Calcic Yermosols have been formed. They contain 25 to over 50% lime. Small areas of loamy Yermosols occur in the lower parts of the plain.

5. *Regosol-Arenosol association of the sandy deserts of the Arabian Peninsula*

Covering about one third of the Arabian Peninsula, this soil region includes the two major sandy deserts, the Rub al-Khali and the Al-Nafud, as well as the adjoining areas which have shallow sandy soils. Rainfall is very scanty and sporadic. In the north it occurs in the winter and spring and in the south during summer. The climate of this region is characterized by extreme aridity, very high winds and very high summer temperatures.

TABLE 4. – SOIL ASSOCIATIONS AND RELATED INFORMATION

Map symbol	Associated soils	Inclusions	Phase	Extension (1 000 ha)	Climate	Occurrence
Af45-2b	Ag Ao	I J		157	1.12	Sri Lanka
Af46-1/2a	Ap G	Jd		57	1.92	Bangladesh
Af46-1/2a	Ap G	Jd		400	1.92	India
Af47-2b	Ap Nd			242	1.92	India
Af48-2ab	Ah Nd	Jd G		2 097	1.92	India
Ah4-2b	Ao	I Jd Od	Stony	132	1.12	Sri Lanka
Ah11-2c	Ao	I Bf		549	1.53	India
Ah12-2bc	Bh Nh	Bd G I		333	2.26, 4.34	Nepal
Ah12-2bc	Bh Nh	Bd G I		142	2.26	India
Ao1-2bc				65	1.91	India
Ao72-2b	Ph			729	10.57	India
Ao73-2bc	Af Bf	I Jd G		938	1.73, 2.41	Sri Lanka
Ao74-2b	Ah	Nd		410	2.31	India
Ao75-2b	Af Nd			697	4.25	India
Ao76-2/3c	I Nd	Ah	Lithic	7 127	1.48, 2.25, 4.34, 9.81	Burma
Ao76-2/3c	I Nd	Ah	Lithic	2 843	2.25	India
Ao77-2a	Af Ag	Jd G		178	1.92	India
Ao78-3c	Ah Bd		Lithic	252	2.31	India
Ao79-a	Ag Lf			484	1.92	India
Ao80-2bc	Ah Pl	Bh Dd		2 665	2.32, 2.26	Bhutan
Ao80-2bc	Ah Pl	Bh Dd		3 272	2.26	India
Ao81-2b	Ah	I	Stony	581	4.32	India
Ao89-2/3b	Af Lf	Fp Gp		9 415	1.48, 2.25, 4.34	Burma
Ao90-2/3c		Ah Bd I	Lithic	17 837	1.13, 1.46, 2.25, 2.32	Burma
Ap19-2b	Af Ag	Jd Gd Od		292	1.12	Sri Lanka
Ap21-2b	Af	I	Petroferric	4 363	1.13, 1.42, 1.14, 1.48, 1.53	India
Bc11-2a	Je Re	Jc Rc		240	2.25, 4.34	Burma
Bc23-2a	Bk Lc	I	Lithic	72	1.13	Sri Lanka
Bc24-2b	Lf Nc	Je		326	1.14	India
Bc25-2c	Lc Ne		Lithic	887	1.91, 4.34	India
Bc26-2c	Ne			258	1.91	India
Bd29-3c	Ah	Ge	Lithic	419	2.26, 4.34	Nepal
Bd29-3c	Ah	Ge	Lithic	2 924	4.25, 2.32	India
Bd32-2bc	Nd Rd		Stony	524	2.26	Bhutan
Bd32-2bc	Nd Rd		Stony	261	2.32	India
Bd34-2bc	Ao Dd I	Bh Bc G O	Stony	5 557	2.26, 2.32	Nepal
Bd35-1/2b	Ao Jd	P Dd G		380	10.57	Nepal
Bd61-2c	Ao	Gd I		1 863	1.92	Bangladesh
Bd61-2c	Ao	Gd I		749	1.24, 1.43, 1.92	Burma
Bd61-2c	Ao	Gd I		1 746	1.92	India
Be65-ab	Bk Lc Re	V Je	Stony	101	6.15	Syria
Be65-ab	Bk Lc Re	V Je	Stony	56	6.15	Lebanon
Be66-2c	Re	I		258	1.91	India
Be66-2/3c	Re	I		122	6.71	Iran

TABLE 4. – SOIL ASSOCIATIONS AND RELATED INFORMATION (*continued*)

Map symbol	Associated soils	Inclusions	Phase	Extension (1 000 ha)	Climate	Occurrence
Be67-3c	Bk Re	I Hh		333	6.72, 8.3	Iran
Be68-3a	Bk Ge	Zo		175	6.62	Iran
Be69-3c	Ao Bd			292	6.62, 6.71, 8.3	Iran
Be70-2/3a	Bg	Ge Je		374	4.21, 6.73, 6.74	Pakistan
Be70-2/3a	Bg	Ge Je		142	4.21	India
Be71-2/3a	Bg	Vc Zo		622	4.22, 4.52, 6.74	Pakistan
Be71-2/3a	Bg	Vc Zo		61	4.21	India
Be72-2a	Lo			765	3.71, 10.57	India
Be72-2c	Lo		Stony	339	3.71, 10.57	India
Be72-2c	Lo		Lithic	952	4.25	India
Be72-2c	Lo		Lithic	48	4.21, 4.25	Pakistan
Be72-3c	Lo		Lithic	301	4.21	Pakistan
Be72-3c	Lo		Lithic	1 559	4.25, 0.57	India
Be73-2c	I	Bk U	Lithic	1 113	6.74, 6.75, 4.25	Pakistan
Be73-2c	I	Bk U	Lithic	29	6.75	India
Be74-2a	Je Re	I		2 117	1.91, 4.32	India
Be74-2a	Je Re	I	Saline	4 218	4.34, 4.32, 4.21	India
Be75-2a	Bk So	Je		1 549	1.91, 4.32	India
Be76-2b	Bk Lo	Vc		4 230	4.24, 4.32	India
Be77-2/3c	Bv Lo			529	4.32	India
Be78-2c	Hh I	Lo Bh	Lithic	2 175	10.57	India
Be79-2a	Ge Lo	Re Je		687	6.74	India
Be80-2a	Lo	Jc Bk		1 481	1.91, 4.34	India
Be81-2a	Ge	Bh		294	4.34, 1.91	Bangladesh
Be81-2a	Ge	Bh		1 581	4.34	India
Be82-a	Lo	Ao Lc		1 517	4.34, 1.92	India
Be83-2a	G Je	Lo Bk		813	4.34	India
Be84-2a	Lo Je	G		50	4.34	Nepal
Be84-2a	Lo Je	G		7 841	4.34	India
Be85-2a	Zo	I	Saline	2 985	4.32, 4.22, 4.21	India
Bf12-3bc	Af Nd	Gd		154	1.12, 1.73	Sri Lanka
Bf17-2c	Ao Fr	I Je	Lithic	4 785	1.24, 1.46, 1.48, 2.25	Burma
Bf17-2c	Ao Fr	I Je	Lithic	48	2.25	India
Bf18-2/3b	Bh Rd	Nd Jd		581	1.12, 1.13	Andaman and Nicobar Is.
Bh10-2a				61	4.34	Bangladesh
Bh10-2a				100	4.34	India
Bh16-2/3c	Ah I	U	Lithic	3 722	1.48, 1.92, 2.25	Burma
Bh16-2/3c	Ah I	U	Lithic	2 233	2.25	India
Bh18-2b	Be		Stony	33	4.34	Nepal
Bh18-2b	Be		Stony	39	4.34	India
Bk33-3c	I	E	Stony	248	6.15, 6.51	Lebanon
Bk34-3b	E	Lc Re Vc		59	6.15	Lebanon
Bk37-2/3c	Be Re	I		1 305	6.62, 6.71, 8.3	Iran
Bk38-1/2b	Jc Kh	Rc De Lo	Stony	30	2.26	Nepal
Bk39-2a	Be Jc	G Zo		636	4.34	India

TABLE 4. – SOIL ASSOCIATIONS AND RELATED INFORMATION (*continued*)

Map symbol	Associated soils	Inclusions	Phase	Extension (1 000 ha)	Climate	Occurrence
Bk40-2a	Je	Jc G		1 388	4.34	India
Bv12-3b	Kh Lc	I Vc		7 396	1.91, 4.34	India
Bv12-3b	Kh Lc	I Vc	Lithic	1 042	1.91, 1.53, 4.34	India
Bv15-3b	Lo Vc	E I	Stony	548	6.87	Syria
E17-3bc	I	Lv V	Stony	142	6.13, 6.82	Jordan
E17-3bc	I	Lv V	Stony	60	6.82	Israel
Fr21-2a	Fo	I Jc Vp		272	1.35	Sri Lanka
Fr22-3b	Bf Fo			10	1.13	Andaman and Nicobar Is.
Gc9-3a	Bg	Jc Od		442	1.91	India
Gc9-3a	Bg	Jc Od		2 136	1.91	Bangladesh
Gd25-2a	Ge	Je		471	1.92	India
Gd26-2a	Jd Zg			23	1.13	Andaman and Nicobar Is.
Ge12-1/2a	Be			467	1.91, 1.92	Bangladesh
Ge12-1/2a	Be			242	4.34, 1.92	India
Ge17-3a	Be Gc	Bc Jc		286	6.62, 6.71	Iran
Ge34-3a	Gm Lg			314	6.71, 8.17	Iran
Ge35-3ab	Be	Lo		75	6.71	Iran
Ge36-3a	V	H Z		122	6.74	Iran
Ge37-2/3a	Gm We	Je Vp		4 188	1.13, 1.46, 1.48, 2.25	Burma
Ge 38-2a		Ne Af Je		923	1.91	Bangladesh
Ge38-2a		Ne Af Je		178	1.91	India
Ge50-2/3a	Je	Jt Oe We		3 202	1.24, 1.46	Burma
Ge50-2/3a	Je	Jt Oe We		4	1.23	Bangladesh
Ge51-2a		Je Jc Be Gh		5 025	1.92, 1.24, 1.91	Bangladesh
Ge51-2a		Je Jc Be Gh		403	1.92	India
Ge52-3a		Gc Jc Jt	Saline	786	1.92, 1.24	Bangladesh
Ge52-3a		Gc Jc Jt	Saline	410	1.24, 1.46	India
Ge53-3a		Gd Od		287	1.92	Bangladesh
Ge53-3a		Gd Od		403	1.92	India
Gh12-2a	Jd	Ao		84	2.25	India
Gh15-2/3a	Vp We	Ge Je Z		1 431	1.48, 1.91, 2.25	Burma
Gh16-2/3a	Ge We	Je		1 576	1.48, 1.91, 2.25, 4.34	Burma
Hh11-2bc	Bv Lc	I		1 775	1.48, 1.91	India
I-bc				1 675	4.34	India
I-Af-Bd-2c			Lithic	1 342	2.32	India
I-B-U				856	10.57	Pakistan
I-B-U				4 672	2.31, 2.32, 10.57	India
I-B-U-2c				2 130	10.57	India
I-B-U-2c			Rock debris	10 739	10.57, 6.79	Afghanistan
I-B-U-2c			Rock debris	1 966	10.57	Pakistan
I-B-U-2c			Rock debris	1 336	10.57	India
I-Bc-2c			Rock debris	111	6.78	Iran

TABLE 4. – SOIL ASSOCIATIONS AND RELATED INFORMATION (*continued*)

Map symbol	Associated soils	Inclusions	Phase	Extension (1 000 ha)	Climate	Occurrence
I-Bc-Lc				5 831	1.42, 1.81, 1.48, 1.91, 1.53, 4.34	India
I-Be-2c			Rock debris	423	2.32	India
I-Be-Lc-b				532	4.32	India
I-Be-Lc-bc				1 975	4.32, 4.24, 4.22	India
I-Be-Lc-2/3c			Stony	63	6.18	Syria
I-Be-Lc-2/3c			Stony	176	6.18, 6.51	Lebanon
I-Bh-U-c			Lithic/rock debris	3 103	2.26, 2.32, 9.82, 10.57	Nepal
I-Bh-U-c			Rock debris/lithic	1 138	10.57	Bhutan
I-Bh-U-c			Lithic/rock debris	123	10.57	Afghanistan
I-Bh-U-c			Lithic/rock debris	3 072	10.57	India
I-Bh-U-2c			Stony	1 610	2.25, 2.32, 9.81	Burma
I-Bh-U-2c			Stony	161	2.32	India
I-Bv-3b				439	1.91, 4.32	India
I-Bv-3c				303	4.32	India
I-E-bc				919	6.13, 6.74	Iraq
I-E-Xk-bc				778	6.13, 3.27	Iraq
I-Gx-2c			Rock debris/saline	423	10.57	India
I-Hh				161	1.91	India
I-Lc				106	1.35	Sri Lanka
I-Lc-2bc				4 211	1.42, 1.81, 1.53, 4.34	India
I-Nd-c				407	1.53	India
I-Ne				2 878	1.48, 1.91, 4.34	India
I-Rc				323	4.22	India
I-Rc-bc				—	—	Yemen, People's Dem. Rep. of (Socotra)
I-Rc-X-c			Stony	1 417	6.62, 6.72, 6.74, 8.3	Iran
I-Rc-Xk-c			Stony	8 744	6.62, 6.74, 6.87, 6.91, 8.3	Iran
I-Rc-Xk-c			Stony	347	6.74	Iraq
I-Rc-Yk-c			Stony	869	3.24, 3.27, 3.71, 6.62, 6.74, 6.87, 6.91, 8.3	Iran
I-Rc-Yk-c			Rock debris	42 196	6.62, 6.74, 6.72, 6.77, 6.78, 6.87, 6.91, 8.3	Iran
I-Rc-Yk-c			Rock debris	27 502	1.92, 3.27, 4.22, 4.32, 6.81, 6.87, 6.92,	Pakistan
I-Rc-Yk-c			Rock debris	3 930	3.27, 6.79, 6.87	Afghanistan
I-Rc-Yk-2c			Rock debris	472	6.74, 6.87	Iran
I-Rc-Zo-c			Stony	2 194	3.71, 6.91	Iran
I-Re-X-c			Stony	86	6.71	Iran
I-Re-Yh-bc			Stony	3 614	3.71, 6.62, 6.74, 6.87, 6.91	Iran
I-Re-Yh-c			Stony	7 105	3.27, 3.71, 6.62, 6.71, 6.72, 6.74, 6.91	Iran
I-X-c			Rock debris	3 330	4.21, 4.52, 6.87, 9.12	Pakistan
I-X-c			Rock debris	16 844	6.78, 10.57, 6.79, 6.74, 6.87	Afghanistan
I-X-2c			Rock debris	67	10.57	Pakistan
I-X-2c			Rock debris	446	10.57	Afghanistan
I-Xk-2c			Rock debris	686	3.71, 6.78	Iran

TABLE 4. – SOIL ASSOCIATIONS AND RELATED INFORMATION (*continued*)

Map symbol	Associated soils	Inclusions	Phase	Extension (1 000 ha)	Climate	Occurrence
I-Xk-2c			Stony	1 687	3.27, 6.87	Syria
I-Xk-2c			Stony	93	6.87	Lebanon
I-Y-bc			Stony	4 846	3.11, 1.82	Yemen Arab Rep.
I-Y-bc			Stony	3 226	5.77, 3.24, 3.11, 3.13	Oman
I-Y-bc			Stony	20 403	3.11, 1.82, 3.24, 3.27	Saudia Arabia
I-Y-bc			Stony	432	3.24, 6.81	Jordan
I-Y-bc			Stony	2 085	3.11, 3.24	Yemen, People's Dem. Rep. of
I-Y-bc			Stony	322	3.24	United Arab Emirates
I-Y-2c			Rock debris	453	10.57	Afghanistan
I-Y-2c			Rock debris	5 753	10.57, 3.71	India
I-Yh-Yk-1/2b			Stony	13 964	1.82, 3.24, 3.27	Saudi Arabia
I-Yh-Yk-1/2b			Stony	6 148	3.24, 3.13, 2.35, 2.34, 1.82, 1.81	Yemen Arab Rep.
I-Yh-Yk-1/2b			Stony	512	3.24	Yemen, People's' Dem. Rep. of
I-Yk				273	3.24	Qatar
I-Yk				30	3.24	Saudi Arabia
I-Yk-1/2a			Petrogypsic	1 238	3.24	Saudi Arabia
I-Yk-2ab			Stony	1 171	6.87	Syria
I-Yk-2ab			Stony	9 899	3.27, 3.24	Saudi Arabia
I-Yk-2ab			Stony	414	3.11	Yemen, People's Dem. Rep. of
I-Yk-2ab			Stony	433	1.82, 2.24, 3.24	Yemen Arab Rep.
I-Yk-2ab			Stony	1 165	3.24, 3.27	Jordan
I-Yk-2/3b			Stony	249	6.81	Jordan
I-Yk-2/3b			Stony	592	3.27, 6.81	Israel
Jc1-2a				1 397	3.24, 6.87	Iraq
Jc3-3a	Z		Saline	219	6.81, 6.87	Iran
Jc29-2/3a	Vc			122	3.24	Iraq
Jc36-2/3a		Bk Z G	Saline	532	3.27, 6.87	Syria
Jc36-2/3a		Bk Z G	Saline	47	3.27	Iraq
Jc37-2a	Qc Yk	G Zo		2 403	6.78, 3.27, 6.79, 6.74	Afghanistan
Jc38-2/3a	Vc Zo Zm		Saline	650	3.24	Iraq
Jc39-2/3a	Rc Vc	Zo Zm		91	3.24	Iraq
Jc40-2/3a	Zm Zo		Saline	117	6.87	Iran
Jc40-2/3a	Zm Zo		Saline	625	3.24, 6.87	Iraq
Jc41-2a	Ge	Zo		189	6.71	Iran
Jc42-2/3a		Je		3 891	3.23, 4.22	Pakistan
Jc42-2/3a		Je		184	4.21	India
Jc43-2a	Rc Zg		Saline	423	1.91	India
Jc44-1/2a	Bk Zo	Rc	Saline	807	4.32	India
Jc45-2a	Be	Lo		1 691	4.21, 4.34	India
Jc46-2a	Je			40	1.13	Sri Lanka
Jc47-2a	Rc	Sg Zg	Saline	20	1.13	Sri Lanka
Jc48-2a	Vc	Bk		807	1.48	India
Jc50-2a		Gc		108	1.91	Bangladesh

TABLE 4. – SOIL ASSOCIATIONS AND RELATED INFORMATION (*continued*)

Map symbol	Associated soils	Inclusions	Phase	Extension (1 000 ha)	Climate	Occurrence
Jc50-2a		Gc		1 442	4.34	India
Jc51-2a	Xl Zo	Xk Vc	Saline	1 017	1.48, 1.91	India
Jc52-2a	Gc	Ge	Saline	341	1.92	Bangladesh
Jc53-2a		Zg	Saline	139	3.71, 6.78	Afghanistan
Jc55-2ab	Bk			42	2.32	India
Jd5-2/3a	Gd	Jt Sg Ws Z		29	1.12	Sri Lanka
Je38-2a		Ge		542	1.91	Bangladesh
Je38-2a		Ge		1 613	1.92	India
Je61-2a		Zo		53	3.27	Iraq
Je61-2a		Zo		1 004	3.11, 3.27	Saudi Arabia
Je61-2a		Zo		75	3.11	Yemen, People's Dem. Rep. of
Je61-2a		Zo		406	3.11, 1.81, 2.34, 3.24	Yemen Arab Rep.
Je64-2/3a	Gd Zg	Jc		92	1.13, 1.35	Sri Lanka
Je65-2/3a		Sg		103	1.13	Sri Lanka
Je66-2a	Gh Zm	Jt	Saline	161	1.13	India
Je67-2a	G	Re Z		1 220	1.42, 1.48	India
Je68-2a	Be Zo	Jt Rc	Saline	471	1.14	India
Je69-2/3a	Gh Lf	Af Zo		694	1.48	India
Je71-2a	Bg G			474	1.91	India
Je75-2a	Gm Jc Lo	Hh Lk		956	4.34	Nepal
Je75-2a	Gm Jc Lo	Hh Lk		265	4.34	India
Je76-2a	Bh Hh U	Bc Lf		136	4.34	Nepal
Je77-1/2a	Bh Gh	Ge Hh Re		1 122	4.34	Nepal
Je77-1/2a	Bh Gh	Ge Hh Re		549	4.34, 2.26	India
Jt3-2a	Zg			45	1.91	India
Jt9-2/3a	G Zo	Je		29	1.48	India
Jt10-3a	Jc Zg	O	Sodic/saline	538	1.24	Bangladesh
Jt10-3a	Jc Zg	O	Sodic/saline	574	1.46, 1.24	India
Jt11-3a		Zg		756	1.24, 1.46	Burma
Lc3-2b				126	1.91	India
Lc5-1a	Vc			2 872	4.32, 4.34, 4.24	India
Lc5-2b	Vc			2 601	1.54, 1.91, 1.53	India
Lc12-2/3ab	Lk Vp	We Z		3 094	1.48, 1.91, 2.25	Burma
Lc33-3bc	Bv E	I	Stony	180	6.13	Israel
Lc33-3bc	Bv E	I	Stony	271	6.13	Jordan
Lc33-3bc	Bv E	I	Stony	226	6.15	Lebanon
Lc46-1b	Bc			1 894	1.91	India
Lc46-2b	Bc			2 236	1.96, 1.91	India
Lc46-2b	Bc		Stony	113	1.91	India
Lc63-3bc	Bk I	Rc	Stony	702	6.12, 6.13, 6.15	Syria
Lc69-3a	Lk	I		558	6.13	Syria
Lc70-1/2b	Lf Vc	I	Lithic	881	4.32	India
Lc71-2b	Lg	Je Lp I S		1 411	1.13, 1.35	Sri Lanka
Lc72-2a	I Lg	Je Lp Ws	Petric	1 107	1.12, 1.13, 1.35	Sri Lanka

TABLE 4. – SOIL ASSOCIATIONS AND RELATED INFORMATION (*continued*)

Map symbol	Associated soils	Inclusions	Phase	Extension (1 000 ha)	Climate	Occurrence
Lc73-2bc	Be	I Je G		443	1.12, 1.35, 1.73	Sri Lanka
Lc74-2b	Sg	I G Z		452	1.12, 1.35	Sri Lanka
Lc75-1b	Vc	I		4 576	1.53, 4.24, 4.34	India
Lc75-2b	Vc	I		11 236	1.42, 1.48, 1.53	India
Lc76-2b	Bc	I		12 068	1.48, 1.91, 1.53	India
Lc77-1/2b	Vc	Ge		113	6.13	Israel
Lc77-1/2b	Vc	Ge		23	6.13	Jordan
Lf10-1bc	Ne			1 694	4.34	India
Lf10-2a	Ne		Petric	281	1.91	India
Lf32-1b		I		1 239	1.91	India
Lf32-3bc		I	Petric	317	2.25	Burma
Lf59-2/3b	Bf	I Je	Stony	786	1.48	Burma
Lf92-1a	Lc Lg			12 507	1.91, 4.34	India
Lf92-1a	Lc Lg		Stony	616	1.91, 4.34	India
Lf92-2a	Lc Lg		Petric	287	1.91	India
Lf94-2a	Lp Vc	I G	Petroferric	1 152	4.34	India
Lf95-1a	Lp Ne	Je		458	1.48	India
Lf95-1a	Lp Ne	Je	Petric	1 239	1.46, 1.91	India
Lf96-2ab	Lg	Lp I Je	Petric	1 000	1.46, 1.91	India
Lk5-3ab	I Lc	E Rc Z	Stony	452	6.13, 6.82	Jordan
Lo5-2a	Zo	So		3 727	4.22, 4.21, 4.34, 4.32	India
Lo34-2a		Zo		452	4.22	India
Lo35-2a	Be			1 220	4.34, 4.21	India
Lo44-1b	Lc			884	4.21	India
Lo45-1a	Lc Sg	Je Be I		192	1.13, 1.35	Sri Lanka
Lo46-1a	Lg	Je I Lc		54	1.13	Sri Lanka
Lo47-1a	Lc Lg	Vc Zo So		1 036	1.42, 1.53	India
Lo47-2a	Lc Lg	Vc Zo So		710	1.48	India
Lo48-2a	Jc	G		297	1.91	India
Lo49-1ab	Be Lk	Jc G		100	1.91	India
Lo49-1b	Be Lk	Jc G		219	1.91	India
Lo49-1b	Be Lk	Jc G	Stony	358	1.91, 4.34	India
Lo49-2a	Be Lk	Jc G		2 346	1.91, 1.46, 4.34	India
Lo49-2c	Be Lk	Jc G	Lithic	733	4.32	India
Lo50-2a	Be Lc	G		74	1.91	India
Lo51-2a	Lf Zo	Je So G		1 881	4.34	India
Lp13-2a	Lc Lf		Petroferric	161	1.53	India
Lv2-3b	Lk Vc	E Bk I		85	6.13	Israel
Nd2-2b	Ao			1 207	1.92	India
Nd46-2ab	Ao	Ge Gh		485	1.91	Bangladesh
Nd47-2b	Fh			268	1.53	India
Nd48-2/3b	G Jd	Af		2 078	1.13, 1.14	India
Nd49-2bc	Ao I	Bf		1 249	1.14	India
Nd50-2b	Lf Lg	I G		2 059	1.14, 1.91, 4.34	India
Nd51-2b	Bf			387	1.48, 1.91	India

TABLE 4. – SOIL ASSOCIATIONS AND RELATED INFORMATION (*continued*)

Map symbol	Associated soils	Inclusions	Phase	Extension (1 000 ha)	Climate	Occurrence
Nd52-2b	Ah			455	1.92	India
Nd53-3bc	Bd Rd			290	1.92	India
Nd53-3bc	Bd Rd			123	2.26	Bhutan
Nd55-2/3b	Af	Ap I	Lithic	4 964	1.13, 1.46, 1.48, 2.25	Burma
Ne53-2ab	Lc Lf			1 968	1.81, 1.48, 1.53	India
Ne53-2b	Lc Lf			1 646	1.48, 1.91, 1.53	India
Ne55-2b	Ah Lf			387	1.81	India
Ne56-2b	Bc Lf			1 275	1.14, 1.91, 4.34	India
Ne56-2b	Bc Lf		Petric	1 029	1.14, 1 48, 1.91	India
Ne57-2a	I Lg			449	1.48, 1.91	India
Ne58-1bc	Bc Lf	Ao		5 799	1.91	India
Ne58-1bc	Bc Lf	Ao	Petric	316	1.91	India
Ne59-2a	Lf Lg	Bc I	Petric	90	1.91	India
Ne59-2ab	Lf Lg	Bc I		55	1.91	India
Ne59-2b	Lf Lg	Bc I		1 433	1.91	India
Nh8-2/3ab	Ao	Ap G		692	2.25	Burma
Od13-a	Gh Jt		Saline	32	1.13	India
Od14-a		Gc Jt		355	1.91	Bangladesh
Qa9-1a			Stony	386	3.24, 6.81	Kuwait
Qa9-1a			Stony	335	3.24	Saudi Arabia
Qa9-1a			Stony	1 281	3.24	Iraq
Qa10-1a	Qc	Gd		36	1.13	Andaman and Nicobar Is.
Qc46-1/2ab	I Y	R	Lithic/stony	1 340	3.11, 3.24	Yemen, People's Dem. Rep. of
Qc46-1/2ab	I Y	R	Lithic/stony	150	3.27	Iraq
Qc46-1/2ab	I Y	R	Lithic/stony	27 055	3.27, 3.24, 3.13	Saudi Arabia
Qc46-1/2ab	Y	R	Lithic/stony	733	3.24	Jordan
Qc46-1/2ab	I Y	R	Lithic/stony	565	3.24	United Arab Emirates
Qc46-1/2ab	I Y	R	Lithic/stony	35	3.24	Kuwait
Qc46-1/2ab	I Y	R	Lithic/stony	270	2.35, 3.24	Yemen Arab Rep.
Qc47-1a	Rc	Yk Z		7 374	3.71, 3.27, 6.87, 6.78	Afghanistan
Qc47-1a	Rc	Yk Z		6	3.71	Iran
Qc47-1a	Rc	Yk Z		489	3.27, 6.87	Pakistan
Qc47-1/2b	Rc	Yk Z	Shifting sand	11 290	3.23, 3.27, 4.22, 4.31	Pakistan
Qc47-1/2b	Rc	Yk Z	Shifting sand	14 808	4.32, 4.31, 4.22, 3.23	India
Qc48-1a	Rc			271	3.23	India
Qc48-1a	Rc			38	3.23	Pakistan
Qc49-1a	Xh	Xk Jc Zo		958	4.22	India
Qc50-1a	Qa Qf	Rd Od Jd		146	1.12	Sri Lanka
Rc1-1ab			Shifting sand	519	3.24, 6.87	Iraq
Rc1-2a				306	6.13, 6.82	Israel
Rc1-2b				84	4.32	India
Rc30-1ab	Qc Yk	Z	Shifting sand	84	3.13	Oman
Rc30-1ab	Qc Yk	Z	Shifting sand	1 868	3.13, 3.24	United Arab Emirates

TABLE 4. – SOIL ASSOCIATIONS AND RELATED INFORMATION (*continued*)

Map symbol	Associated soils	Inclusions	Phase	Extension (1 000 ha)	Climate	Occurrence
Rc30-1ab	Qc Yk	Z	Shifting sand	40 414	3.27, 3.24	Saudi Arabia
Rc30-1ab	Qc Yk	Z	Shifting sand	902	3.24, 3.13	Yemen Arab Rep.
Rc30-1ab	Qc Yk	Z	Shifting sand	1 436	3.24, 3.11	Yemen, People's Dem. Rep. of
Rc30-1ab	Qc Yk	Z	Shifting sand	343	3.24	Qatar
Rc31-1/2ab	Z			359	3.13	United Arab Emirates
Rc31-1/2ab	Z			6 142	3.13	Saudi Arabia
Rc31-1/2ab	Z			30	3.24	Iran
Rc31-1/2ab	Z			77	3.13	Oman
Rc32-1ab	Yy		Petrogypsic	66	6.87	Iraq
Rc33-3bc	I Yk	Zo	Stony	10 908	3.71, 6.72, 6.74, 6.78, 6.87, 6.91, 8.3	Iran
Rc34-3b	Gc Xk			114	6.78	Iran
Rc35-1a		Qc		92	6.71	Iran
Rc35-1/2bc		Qc		267	3.27	Iran
Rc36-3c	Xh	Zo	Stony	694	6.62, 6.72, 6.74, 6.91	Iran
Rc37-3c	I	Zo		9 586	3.15, 3.24, 3.27, 6.74, 6.81, 6.87	Iran
Rc38-1a		Zo	Shifting sand	3 747	3.15, 3.27, 3.71, 6.91	Iran
Rc38-1a		Zo	Shifting sand	116	6.87	Iraq
Rc40-2b	Xk			1 085	4.21	Pakistan
Rd23-1a	G Je	Qa Rc Zo		1 468	1.13, 1.42, 1.14	India
Rd24-1a	Je Zo	Rc		826	1.13, 1.48	India
Rd25-1a	Jd	Nd		113	1.14	India
Rd26-1a	Jt Zo			261	1.48	India
Rd27-1a	Je	Ne		284	1.48	India
Rd28-1a	Je			74	2.26	Bhutan
Rd28-1a	Je			445	2.26	India
Rd29-1a	Be Gh	Ag Jd		161	4.34, 2.26	India
Rd30-2b	Bc Rc	Ne Fo	Stony	1 298	2.26, 4.34	Nepal
Rd30-2b	Bc Rc	Ne Fo	Stony	523	4.21, 4.34	India
Rd31-1/2b	Bf Jd			29	1.12, 1.13	Andaman and Nicobar Is.
Re41-2/3c	I	Be T	Stony	42	6.62	Iran
Re46-2c	Be Rd		Stony	491	4.21	India
Re53-2b	Lo			281	4.21	India
Re66-1a	Qa Rc	Zg		169	1.13	Sri Lanka
Vc1-3a				94	6.13	Syria
Vc1-3a				1 031	6.13, 6.87	Iraq
Vc13-2/3b	Bv			5 315	1.91, 4.32	India
Vc21-3a	Bc Lc			4 424	1.53, 4.34, 4.32	India
Vc21-3b	Bc Lc			678	4.24	India
Vc42-2/3a	Bv Lc	Bk G Jc I		102	6.15	Lebanon
Vc43-3ab	Bv	I		35 137	1.42, 1.48, 1.91, 1.53, 4.34, 4.24, 4.32	India
Vc44-3a	So Zo		Saline	152	1.54	India
Vc45-3a		G		4 601	1.48, 1.91, 1.53, 4.34	India

TABLE 4. – SOIL ASSOCIATIONS AND RELATED INFORMATION (*continued*)

Map symbol	Associated soils	Inclusions	Phase	Extension (1 000 ha)	Climate	Occurrence
Vc46-3a	Bv	Lc		186	6.13	Israel
Vc46-3a	Bv	Lc		42	6.13	Jordan
Vc46-3a	Bv	Lc		31	6.13	Syria
Vc47-3b	Bk Bv	I Lc	Stony	654	3.27, 6.13, 6.15	Syria
Vc47-3b	Bk Bv	I Lc	Stony	12	6.51	Lebanon
Vc47-3b	Bk Bv	I Lc	Stony	13	3.27	Jordan
Vc48-3a	Gc	Jc Z		179	6.87	Syria
Vc49-3a		Jc Zo		447	6.87	Iraq
Vc50-3ab	Xk			222	6.74	Iraq
Vc51-3a	Lc Ne			29	1.12, 1.13	Andaman and Nicobar Is.
Vp20-3a	Vc			6 667	1.42, 1.48, 1.91, 1.53, 4.34	India
Vp39-3b	Bv	Rc Bk		94	6.15	Syria
Vp40-3a	Je Vc	Zg		678	1.48, 1.91, 2.25	Burma
Vp42-3a		Jc G		3 633	1.53	India
Vp42-3a		Jc G	Saline	387	1.53	India
Xh 7-2/3ab	Rc			1 642	6.72, 6.74, 6.78, 6.87, 6.91	Iran
Xh12-2a	Xk		Saline	5 069	4.32, 4.22	India
Xh18-bc	E Xk		Stony	566	6.74, 10.57	Afghanistan
Xh18-bc	E Xk		Stony	73	6.74	Pakistan
Xh30-3a	Zo	Zg	Saline	44	6.74	Iran
Xh31-3a	Gc Rc	Zo		1 372	6.74, 6.81, 6.87	Iran
Xh32-3ab	Xk	Gc Rc		775	6.77, 6.78	Iran
Xh33-3a	Xk	Rc I		800	6.62, 6.74	Iran
Xh34-3a	Rc Zo		Saline	472	6.74, 6.87, 6.91	Iran
Xh35-3a	Xk	Rc Zo		594	6.78	Iran
Xh37-3a	Rc Xk Zo	V	Saline	514	6.62, 6.72, 6.91	Iran
Xh38-3a	Bc			136	6.72, 6.74	Iran
Xh39-3ab	Rc	Bc		517	6.62, 6.74	Iran
Xh40-3a	Rc Zo	Gc Hc	Sodic	450	6.74, 6.87	Iran
Xh41-3b	Rc	Jc Lc	Stony	131	6.78	Iran
Xh42-2/3a		Zo	Saline	1 513	6.87	Pakistan
Xh43-2/3a	Yh Yk	Zo		332	4.32, 4.31	India
Xh44-2a	Yh Yk			897	1.91	India
Xk4-1b				56	3.71	Iran
Xk4-1b			Stony	107	6.78	Afghanistan
Xk4-1b			Stony	128	3.71	Iran
Xk4-2b				847	3.71, 6.78	Afghanistan
Xk5-2/3a	Rc		Stony	2 167	3.24, 6.74, 6.91, 8.3	Iran
Xk5-3ab	Rc			2 325	6.62, 6.72, 6.74, 6.78, 6.87	Iran
Xk9-2/3a	Xy			1 473	6.87	Syria
Xk9-2/3a	Xy			847	6.87	Iraq
Xk19-2a		Zo		622	4.22	Pakistan
Xk19-2a		Zo		2 711	4.22	India

TABLE 4. – SOIL ASSOCIATIONS AND RELATED INFORMATION (*continued*)

Map symbol	Associated soils	Inclusions	Phase	Extension (1 000 ha)	Climate	Occurrence
Xk21-3b	Xl	I		123	6.13	Israel
Xk22-2/3b	Xl	G I Z	Saline	106	6.82	Jordan
Xk25-2c	I Rc	Lc Z	Stony	1 043	3.27, 6.87	Jordan
Xk25-2c	I Rc	Lc Z	Stony	35	6.87	Syria
Xk26-2/3a		Rc Vc		344	6.87	Iraq
Xk26-2/3a		Rc Vc		1 422	3.24, 6.87	Syria
Xk26-2/3a		Rc Vc	Stony	126	6.87	Syria
Xk26-2/3a		Rc Vc	Stony	68	6.18	Lebanon
Xk27-2ab	Xl	Rc I	Petrocalcic	1 462	6.12, 6.87	Syria
Xk28-b	Vc	I	Lithic	31	6.87	Iran
Xk28-b	Vc	I	Lithic	1 272	6.13, 6.87	Iraq
Xk29-ab	E	Vc	Lithic	31	6.74	Iraq
Xk32-3a	Gc Rc			258	6.74, 6.87	Iran
Xk33-3a	Rc Zo		Saline	56	6.87	Iran
Xk34-2ab	Rc	Bc		231	6.74	Iran
Xk35-2/3a	So		Saline	216	4.21	Pakistan
Xk35-3a	So		Sodic	236	6.74, 6.91	Iran
Xk36-3a	Rc	Zo		278	6.87	Iran
Xk37-2b	Zo			19	6.78	Iran
Xy4-2/3a	Xk	Rc I	Stony	78	6.87	Iraq
Xy4-2/3a	Xk	Rc I	Stony	1 897	6.87	Syria
Xy5-a	I Rc	Vc		656	6.13, 6.87	Iraq
Y13-ab	R		Saline	521	3.71	Iran
Y14-1a		Z		44	6.91	Iran
Yh3-1/2a	I			16 788	3.24, 3.27, 3.13	Saudi Arabia
Yh22-1ab	Qc Yk	Rc Jc Z		2 461	3.11	Yemen Arab Rep.
Yh22-1ab	Qc Yk	Rc Jc Z		1 738	3.11	Saudi Arabia
Yh22-1ab	Qc Yk	Rc Jc Z		1 406	3.11, 3.24	Yemen, People's Dem. Rep. of
Yh22-1ab	Qc Yk	Rc Jc Z		466	3.13, 3.11	Oman
Yh22-1ab	Qc Yk	Rc Jc Z		60	3.13, 3.24	United Arab Emirates
Yh23-2ab	Rc Yk	Zo		4 664	6.78, 3.71, 6.79	Afghanistan
Yh23-2ab	Rc Yk	Zo		386	6.91	Iran
Yh23-3a	Rc Yk	Zo		175	6.91	Iran
Yh24-3a		Jc		139	3.15	Iran
Yh25-3a	Yk	Zo Rc	Saline	153	6.62	Iran
Yh26-2/3a		Zo	Saline	7 510	3.23, 4.22	Pakistan
Yh26-2/3a		Zo	Saline	3 982	4.22	India
Yh27-2a	Zo	Jc Qc		5 645	3.23, 4.22, 4.31	Pakistan
Yk6-3ab	I		Petrocalcic	563	3.27	Iraq
Yk24-2/3bc	I	R Z Yy	Lithic/stony	353	6.81, 6.82	Israel
Yk24-2/3bc	I	R Z Yy	Stony/lithic	26	6.82	Jordan
Yk25-1/2a	I Yl	Jc Z	Lithic/stony	9 648	3.24, 3.13, 3.11	Oman
Yk25-1/2a	I Yl	Jc Z	Lithic/stony	17 376	3.24, 3.27	Saudi Arabia
Yk25-1/2a	I Yl	Jc Z	Lithic/stony	60	3.35	Bahrain

TABLE 4. – SOIL ASSOCIATIONS AND RELATED INFORMATION (*continued*)

Map symbol	Associated soils	Inclusions	Phase	Extension (1 000 ha)	Climate	Occurrence
Yk25-1/2a	I Yl	Jc Z	Lithic/stony	1 360	3.24	Qatar
Yk25-1/2a	I Yl	Jc Z	Lithic/stony	11 233	3.24, 3.11, 3.13	Yemen, People's Dem. Rep. of
Yk25-1/2a	I Yl	Jc Z	Lithic/stony	1 956	2.35, 3.24, 1.82, 3.11	Yemen Arab Rep.
Yk26-1a	Qc			563	3.24, 3.27	Iraq
Yk26-1a	Qc		Petrocalcic	398	3.24	United Arab Emirates
Yk26-1a	Qc		Petrocalcic	125	3.27	Iraq
Yk26-1ab	Qc		Petrocalcic	2 397	3.13	Oman
Yk26-1ab	Qc		Petrocalcic	502	3.13, 3.24	United Arab Emirates
Yk26-1ab	Qc		Petrocalcic	1 123	3.13	Yemen, People's Dem. Rep. of
Yk26-1ab	Qc		Petrocalcic	9 774	3.24, 3.27, 3.13	Saudi Arabia
Yk27-2a	Z	I		1 376	3.27, 3.24, 3.13	Saudi Arabia
Yk28-1a	Rc	I	Stony	3 113	3.13, 3.24, 3.11	Yemen, People's Dem. Rep. of
Yk28-1a	Rc	I	Stony	395	3.13, 3.24, 1.82, 3.24	United Arab Emirates
Yk28-1a	Rc	I	Stony	3 462	3.24, 3.13, 3.11	Oman
Yk28-1a	Rc	I	Stony	1 424	3.13, 3.24	Yemen Arab Rep.
Yk28-1a	Rc	I	Stony	55	3.24	Jordan
Yk28-1a	Rc	I	Stony	144	3.27	Iraq
Yk28-1a	Rc	I	Stony	379	3.24, 6.81	Kuwait
Yk28-1a	Rc	I	Stony	19 527	3.27	Saudi Arabia
Yk29-1/2a	Rc	Z	Stony	987	3.24, 3.27	Saudi Arabia
Yk30-bc	I	Rc		5 763	6.87, 3.27	Afghanistan
Yk31-2/3ab	Rc	I Jc Zo		6 766	3.27, 6.87, 6.78	Afghanistan
Yk31-2/3ab	Rc	I Jc Zo		1 472	3.71, 6.81, 6.87, 6.91	Iran
Yk32-a	I Yl		Stony	1 853	3.27	Saudi Arabia
Yk32-a	I Yl		Stony	7 622	3.24, 3.27	Iraq
Yk32-a	I Yl		Lithic	176	3.24	Saudi Arabia
Yk32-a	I Yl		Lithic	5 260	3.24, 3.27	Iraq
Yk34-b	I	Yy	Petrogypsic	1 206	3.27, 6.87	Iraq
Yk34-b	I	Yy	Petrogypsic	42	6.87	Iran
Yk35-3a	Rc Zo		Saline	1 353	3.27, 3.71, 6.81, 6.87, 6.91	Iran
Yk36-2/3a	Rc Zo	I	Stony	562	4.22, 3.23	India
Yk36-2/3a	Rc Zo	I	Stony	9 205	3.15, 3.24, 3.27, 3.71, 6.81, 6.87	Iran
Yk36-2/3a	Rc Zo	I	Stony	236	3.27	Afghanistan
Yk36-2/3a	Rc Zo	I	Stony	7 428	1.92, 3.23, 3.27, 4.22, 6.81, 6.84, 6.87	Pakistan
Yk37-3ab	Zo	I	Stony	1 492	3.71, 6.74, 6.78	Iran
Yk38-3a	Rc Yh	Zo	Stony	8 591	3.24, 3.71, 6.74, 6.91, 8.3	Iran
Yk39-3a	Qc	Rc Zo		216	3.23	Pakistan
Yk40-2/3a	Zo		Saline	13	4.31	India
Yk40-2/3a	Zo		Saline	1 627	1.92, 4.31	Pakistan
Yk41-2a	Rc	Yy Zo		161	4.22, 3.23	India
Yk42-2a		Zo		1 161	3.23, 4.22	Pakistan

TABLE 4. – SOIL ASSOCIATIONS AND RELATED INFORMATION (*continued*)

Map symbol	Associated soils	Inclusions	Phase	Extension (1 000 ha)	Climate	Occurrence
Yl19-3ab	I Yk	Rc	Stony	1 372	3.27	Syria
Yl19-3ab	I Yk	Rc	Stony	2 550	3.27	Iraq
Yl19-3ab	I Yk	Rc	Stony	8 123	3.27	Saudi Arabia
Yl19-3ab	I Yk	Rc	Stony	4 713	3.24, 3.27	Jordan
Yl19-3ab	I Yk	Rc	Stony	654	3.13, 3.24	Yemen Arab Rep.
Yl19-3ab	I Yk	Rc	Stony	369	3.24	Yemen, People's Dem. Rep. of
Yl20-3a	Yk	Yy		97	3.27	Iraq
Yl20-3a	Yk	Yy		28	3.27	Syria
Yt3-3a		Zo		6	3.71	Afghanistan
Yy7-2/3a	Yk Zo	Jc	Petrogypsic	161	3.27	Jordan
Yy7-2/3a	Yk Zo	Jc	Petrogypsic	51	3.27	Saudi Arabia
Yy10-2ab	I Yk		Petrogypsic	786	3.13, 3.24	Oman
Yy10-2ab	I Yk		Petrogypsic	4 885	3.13, 3.24	Yemen, People's Dem. Rep. of
Yy10-2/3a	I Yk		Petrogypsic	3 515	3.27	Syria
Yy10-2/3a	I Yk		Petrogypsic	4 269	3.27, 6.87	Iraq
Yy11-2/3a	Yk	I	Stony	774	3.27	Syria
Yy12-a	I	Yk	Petrogypsic/stony	1 809	3.24, 3.27, 6.87	Iraq
Yy12-a	I	Yk	Petrogypsic/stony	95	3.24	Saudi Arabia
Yy12-a	I	Yk	Petrogypsic/stony	591	3.24, 6.81	Kuwait
Yy13-a	I		Stony	516	3.27, 6.87	Iraq
Zg3-2/3a	Zo			842	3.11	Saudi Arabia
Zg3-2/3a	Zo			290	3.13, 3.11	Oman
Zg3-2/3a	Zo			670	3.24	United Arab Emirates
Zg3-2/3a	Zo			225	3.24	Qatar
Zg3-3a	Zo			377	3.23, 3.27, 6.87	Pakistan
Zg3-3a	Zo			6	6.77	Iran
Zg4-3a		Je Jt		634	1.46	Burma
Zg6-2/3a				495	1.92	Pakistan
Zg6-2/3a				562	1.91, 4.31	India
Zg13-2/3a	So Zt	Yy Jc		95	4.31	Pakistan
Zg13-2/3a	So Zt	Yy Jc		1 820	4.32, 4.31	India
Zg14-2a	S	Jt Ws Vp	Sodic	180	1.35	Sri Lanka
Zo7-2/3a	Zg			191	3.27	Afghanistan
Zo7-2/3a	Zg			1 056	3.24, 6.87	Iraq
Zo7-2/3a	Zg			1 283	3.71, 6.81	Iran
Zo7-3a	Zg			32	4.32	India
Zo10-2/3a	Jc	Yk		35	3.24	Jordan
Zo18-2ab	I	Yk		2 333	3.24	Saudi Arabia
Zo19-1/2ac	I	Rc Qc		889	3.24	Saudi Arabia
Zo19-1/2ac	I	Rc Qc		419	3.13, 3.24	United Arab Emirates
Zo20-1/2a	Yh	Rc		1 938	3.11, 3.24	Saudi Arabia
Zo21-3a	So Yk	Jc		17 272	3.24, 3.71, 3.15, 6.74, 6.77, 6.81, 6.87, 6.91	Iran
Zo21-3a	So Yk	Jc		2 733	3.27	Afghanistan

TABLE 4. – SOIL ASSOCIATIONS AND RELATED INFORMATION (*concluded*)

Map symbol	Associated soils	Inclusions	Phase	Extension (1 000 ha)	Climate	Occurrence
Zo22-2/3a	Zm	Jc Vc		2 541	3.24, 3.27, 6.87	Iraq
Zo22-2/3a	Zm	Jc Vc		22	6.81	Iran
Zo23-2/3a	Jc Vc Zm			2 966	3.24	Iraq
Zo24-3b	Rc Yk			931	3.71, 6.91	Iran
Zo25-3a	Zt	Rc		661	3.71	Iran
Zo26-3a	Zg Zt	Ge		306	6.72, 6.77	Iran
Zo27-3a	Yk Zg			3 772	3.15, 3.71	Iran
Zo27-3a	Yk Zg			111	6.84	Pakistan
Zo28-3a	Zt	Zg Jc		116	6.81	Iraq
Zo28-3a	Zt	Zg Jc		564	6.81	Iran
Zo28-3a	Zt	Zg Jc		209	6.81	Kuwait
Zo29-3a	Rc Yh	Jc		25	3.23	Pakistan
Zo29-3a	Rc Yh	Jc		368	3.23	India
Zo30-2a		Jc		39	1.48	India
Zo31-3a	So		Sodic	61	1.46	India
Zo32-3a	Jt So			97	1.24	India
Zo33-2/3a		I Yk		28	6.81	Israel
Zo33-2/3a		I Yk		39	6.81	Jordan

The main soils are Calcaric Regosols and Cambic Arenosols. The Arenosols are mostly shallow and stony, whereas the Regosols occur on sand dunes and sand ridges. These dunes and ridges occur in four different forms: crescent-shaped transversal dunes (barchans); longitudinal sand ridges which are often partially stabilized by sparse vegetation; long, sharp-crested dunes (urugs) separated by broad sand valleys; and sand mountains, which are massifs 50 to 300 metres high, often with superimposed giant barchans (Paseur, 1971). The stabilized dunes predominate in the north where the rainfall is about 100 mm or more. In the eastern part of the Rub al-Khali the flat areas between the dunes have Solonchaks with hygroscopic salts.

6. *Solonchak-Fluvisol association of the Mesopotamian plain*

This soil region covers the plain area of Iraq and the adjoining coastal plain of Iran. The main soils are Orthic Solonchaks and Calcaric Fluvisols formed in Holocene and Pleistocene alluvium. The Solonchaks cover about three fourths of the total area and invariably contain gypsum. As the rainfall is very scanty (less than 250 mm), irrigation is essential for growing crops.

The soils are mainly silty and are strongly calcareous, containing about 20% lime. The soil pattern is silt loams on levee deposits and silty clay loams and clays in flat basins. As there is very little vegetation, the soil has very little tubular porosity or organic matter. In the northwest the water table is generally deep, but is high in spots. The lower central part has a high water table and marshes. In the southeastern part is a delta area which comprises mainly estuarine deposits, with silty soils on levees and clays on flats. All the date palm groves are on levee soils.

7. *Lithosol-Xerosol association of western and northern Iran*

Covering the major part of the Zagros and Elburz mountain ranges, this soil region is an area of hills and intermontane valleys. It is a semiarid area with 300 to about 550 mm annual precipitation occurring mostly in the winter and spring. High mountain areas in the western part may receive up to 700 mm of rainfall. Elevations range from 1 000 to 3 000 metres, and a few mountains exceed

3 000 metres. The vegetation is open oak forest in high mountain areas and scrub formations at low elevations. Grasses are an important component of the vegetation.

The main rocks are Tertiary limestone and marl with some calcareous shale and sandstone. Gypsum and other anhydrites are interbedded with marl. A large part of the area is covered by Quaternary alluvium which is usually highly calcareous. In the north a considerable part of the area is covered by basalt and gneiss.

The soils are mainly Lithosols on steep slopes and Haplic or Calcic Xerosols in valleys. In some places the Xerosols are stony or gravelly. All are calcareous. Stony Regosols occur on stony colluvial deposits on hill slopes.

A typical soil pattern is represented by the Karkheh river basin (ELC and Ab van Khak, 1971). The lower parts of mountain slopes have gravelly or stony soils (Regosols) where the slope is 3 to 8% and gravelly loams (Xerosols) on 1 to 3% slopes. Pleistocene alluvial terraces with gently sloping to rolling relief have loamy Xerosols with an incipient argillic B horizon. These Xerosols usually have a pronounced lime accumulation at about 60 to 100 cm or even shallower depth (Veenenbos, 1968). The gently sloping parts of mountain plains have loamy Xerosols with only a cambic B horizon, and there are some clayey Solonchaks in the lower parts. The Solonchaks are usually poorly drained. In some irrigated areas thick deposits of irrigation silt overlie the Xerosols. Calcaric Fluvisols occur in narrow strips along the rivers. In higher rainfall areas at high altitudes Calcaric Phaeozems are found (Dewan and Famouri, 1964). In the lower rainfall areas the Xerosols intergrade to Yermosols.

8. Cambisol-Gleysol association of the humid area of Iran

This soil region covers the northern part of the Elburz mountains and the coastal plain along the Caspian Sea. It is a subhumid to humid area with rainfall of 600 to 1 000 mm; some parts receive up to 2 000 mm per annum. Most of the area is hilly with elevations ranging from a few hundred metres to more than 4 000 metres. The natural vegetation is oak forest.

The main soils on hillsides are Calcaric Cambisols developed from limestone, dolomite and marl. Some calcareous shale and sandstone are also found, and loess deposits occur in some places. In the western part where rainfall is higher there are Eutric Cambisols. The upper parts of mountain slopes have Lithosols and Lithic Cambisols. On the coastal plain the major soils are Eutric Gleysols. A narrow strip of Calcaric Regosols occurs along the coast in the central part of the area.

9. Lithosol-Regosol-Yermosol association of Iran, Afghanistan and Pakistan

Covering the arid parts of Iran and Pakistan and the whole of Afghanistan except a small part of the Hindu Kush, this is one of the most extensive soil regions. The climate is extremely arid; mean annual rainfall is less than 300 mm and in most places it does not exceed 150 mm. The vegetation consists of sparse scrub or steppe formations with some grasses in favourable locations.

The main rocks are Tertiary limestone, marl and calcareous sandstone and shale. Quaternary fluvial and lacustrine deposits occupy valleys. Metamorphic rocks cover a large area in central Afghanistan and small areas in northern, central and southern Iran.

The main soils are Lithosols on hill slopes, stony Regosols on colluvial slopes, Yermosols on piedmont plains and Solonchaks in the playas of closed basins. In some places Regosols occur on sand dunes. The soil pattern is generally governed by the depositional character and the age of the parent material as well as the rock type (FAO, 1971a; Sanders et al., 1968). The mountain slopes are generally bare or have Lithosols. On limestone mountains bare rocks are predominant, while areas of sandstone, shale and marl are mostly covered by Lithosols. The lower parts of mountain slopes have stony Regosols or gravelly Yermosols. The valleys have piedmont alluvial deposits of Pleistocene and subrecent age. The gently sloping parts of the valleys have loamy and silty soils with a structural B horizon (Haplic Yermosols) if the alluvium is of subrecent age. In Pleistocene deposits the soils also have a calcic horizon (Calcic Yermosols). Pleistocene gravel terraces in higher parts of valleys are dissected by later erosion. The soils are gravelly loams with a calcic horizon. The lower parts of many valleys are occupied by playas with clayey Solonchaks, formed by the evaporation of runoff coming from higher areas, particularly in Iran. Fluvisols occur along streams. Some Xerosols are found in high altitude areas with low temperatures and more than 200 mm rainfall (e.g. central Afghanistan).

10. Yermosol-Xerosol association of Pakistan and northwestern India

This soil region covers nearly all of the Indus plains and the semiarid part of northwestern India. Precipitation ranges from about 100 mm in the central part of the Indus plains to about 600 mm in the northeast and southeast. Elevations range from sea level to 300 metres.

In the northern and eastern parts of this region the soils are mainly Calcic and Haplic Xerosols. They have developed in silty and sandy Pleistocene alluvium under subtropical scrub savanna and open forest with considerable grass cover. The soils are well developed, probably owing to the heavy monsoon rains. Rainfall ranges from 500 mm to about 350 mm in the Xerosol belt. In the southeast, Xerosols are formed in alluvium. The dominant soils in the lower rainfall areas are Haplic Yermosols formed mostly in subrecent alluvium. In the Indus plains the soils are well developed as the soil water regime is strongly influenced by regular floods. Scattered patches of Gleysols and Solonetz occur in this region, especially in the Xerosol belt. The Gleysols occur in the lowest-lying areas while the Solonetz occupy slightly higher terrain. Fluvisols occur on young alluvium in strips along rivers. In the Indus delta flood plain, which extends to about 70 km from the coast, Solonchaks occupy a considerable area. Near the coast they become dominant. In the south there is a large area of Solonchaks formed by sea water flooding in the past.

11. *Arenosol-Regosol association of the Thar and Thal deserts*

The Thar and Thal deserts are areas of thick Pleistocene sand deposits. There are sand dunes and ridges of various shapes and heights. The main soils are Cambic Arenosols with inclusions of loamy Haplic Xerosols and Yermosols. Calcaric Regosols predominate in areas with less than 200 mm rainfall.

An old terrace of the Indus river, the Thal area was modified by the wind to form sand dunes 5 to 15 metres high. These dunes occur in three forms: longitudinal ridge-like sief dunes; honeycomb-shaped alveolar dunes, and rake-shaped transversal dunes formed by irregular, non-interconnecting ridges (Ahmad *et al.*, 1968). The sand ridges are stabilized by scrub vegetation except in the southern part where the dune crests consist of loose sand. The soils are mainly Cambic Arenosols. Calcaric Regosols occur in the south were precipitation is less than 200 mm. In the north, where precipitation is more than 200 mm, loamy Xerosols occur in 10 to 20% of the area of interdunal valleys.

The Thar desert consists of longitudinal sand dunes 15 to 40 metres high which are stabilized by shrub vegetation. The high sand dunes are often separated by hummocky sand plains in which there are low dunes 1 to 2 metres high (FAO, 1971c). The dominant soils are Cambic Arenosols, which are associated with loamy Yermosols or even Xerosols in some parts of the sand plains. In some places there are petrocalcic and petrogypsic horizons which

seem to be remnants of Pleistocene soils. In areas of less than 200 mm rainfall Calcaric Regosols tend to predominate as the dune crests have mostly loose sand. In the central part of the Thar there is a fairly extensive area of Haplic Yermosols.

12. *Cambisol-Luvisol association of the northern Indo-Gangetic plain*

This region at the foot of the Himalayas is the subhumid part of the Indo-Gangetic plain. Rainfall ranges between 600 and 1 000 mm except in the eastern part, which receives up to 2 500 mm per annum. Limited areas in the west receive only about 400 mm. The region has a subpiedmont character, as it consists of braided Pleistocene and Holocene river deposits which are generally loamy. The area is nearly level or undulating with elevations ranging from 300 to 500 metres.

The main soils are Eutric Cambisols which developed in calcareous alluvium of mixed mineralogy. Although the lime content is quite deeply leached, traces of free lime keep the pH at around 8, probably owing to the calcareous dust brought in by early summer storms before the onset of the monsoons. The dust comes from the alluvium of the Indus and Ganges rivers and from the Thar desert. In addition to the Cambisols, there are some strips of Calcaric Fluvisols formed on the young river deposits. In the west there are Calcaric Regosols formed on loess and Haplic Xerosols developed in loess and alluvium.

The Cambisols have developed under open forest and grass cover. The parent material is sandy or loamy Pleistocene alluvium or subrecent loamy deposits. Soil formation took place under conditions of good drainage. Locally there are areas of clayey Gleysols which occupy strips of low-lying land or piedmont basins. In some places the soils are undergoing erosion.

In the western part of the plain (Potwar upland area) the Regosols are formed by extensive erosion, which has removed the soil profile and exposed the unaltered loess deposit. The landscape is badly dissected with considerable areas of gullied land. Only a few patches have Eutric Cambisols. A small part of the area in the west has Haplic Xerosols developed from sandstone. In the extreme western part of this region the Peshawar valley has mainly Xerosols, but Cambisols occur in subhumid areas with more than 500 mm rainfall.

13. *Vertisol-Cambisol association of peninsular India*

Covering the northwestern part of peninsular India, this soil region includes extensive areas of Vertisols intercalated with strips of Cambisols. The soils developed mainly from Cretaceous-Eocene basalt or in alluvium derived from it. In some areas they occur on Precambrian gneiss. Elevations range between 200 and 1 000 metres. The climate is tropical and subtropical, subhumid to semiarid, with annual rainfall ranging from 500 to 1 500 mm.

The Vertisols (mostly Chromic Vertisols) occur in nearly level or low-lying areas under grass cover. Their depth exceeds 150 cm in low-lying areas and ranges from 100 to 150 cm in higher terrain. Pellic Vertisols occupy only a small portion of the entire area. Within this vast, nearly continuous Vertisol area are strips of Vertic Cambisols, which usually occur on high undulating ground. They are developed under grass cover and open forest of *Acacia* and *Tectona grandis*. The Vertisols and Vertic Cambisols are slightly to moderately calcareous (Raychaudhuri, 1963). In the northwest there is a considerable area of Eutric Cambisols formed in alluvium derived from basalt and the Precambrian rocks (mainly gneiss, schist and limestone) of the Aravalli mountains. Some admixture of aeolian sand is noted as the texture is sandy loam to clay loam. The soils are mainly noncalcareous, but have a slightly alkaline reaction.

14. *Luvisol-Nitosol association of Sri Lanka and peninsular India*

This soil region extends over the eastern and southern parts of peninsular India and all of Sri Lanka. The soils are mainly Luvisols and Nitosols which have developed from Precambrian gneiss and granite. Being an old stable land mass, this area represents peneplains. Some remnants of very old (probably Tertiary) peneplains have Plinthic Acrisols. Elevations range between 200 and 800 metres. The hills near the coasts of India and in Sri Lanka are 1 000 to 2 000 metres high and in a few areas are higher. The climate is mainly tropical subhumid. The southwestern part of Sri Lanka and a strip on the west coast of India are humid. The vegetation varies, according to the rainfall, from tropical wet evergreen forest to moist deciduous forest and dry deciduous forest.

The major part of the region is covered by Chromic Luvisols, but Ferric Luvisols also occur in the northeast. Nitosols are the next most extensive soils, occurring in the high rainfall areas along the west coast and in the northeastern part of India, and in some areas of Sri Lanka. Some level basins have Vertisols, and areas of young flood plains (mainly near the coasts) have Fluvisols. Associated with the Nitosols are some areas of Acrisols, mostly Plinth-ic Acrisols. Lithosols associated with Luvisols and Nitosols occur in some places.

On the west coast of India a belt about 80 km wide has mainly Eutric and Dystric Nitosols which have developed under tropical evergreen and deciduous forests. The relief is generally undulating to rolling. In the high rainfall area in eastern India where the surface is nearly level, Ferric Luvisols predominate. In southern India Chromic Luvisols are the most extensive soils, with Lithosols on hills. Vertisols occurring in areas of level old alluvium account for a small percentage of the total area. Patches of Plinthic Acrisols occur all along the east coast. On the coasts there are strips of Dystric Regosols developed on coastal sands. Eutric Fluvisols occur in the flood plains of rivers near the coast.

In Sri Lanka Chromic Luvisols and Dystric Nitosols are dominant in the south. In the southwest there are some Vertisols and a strip of Dystric Regosols developed on coastal sands. Humic Acrisols occur in the central mountain area. The northern part has Lithosols and associated Chromic Luvisols, with Dystric Nitosols occurring in undulating areas. In the extreme north and northwest Pellic Vertisols occur in nearly level areas.

15. *Fluvisols of the Ganges-Brahmaputra delta*

Extending over nearly all of Bangladesh and the southeastern part of West Bengal state in India, this soil region includes the flood plains and delta of the Ganges and Brahmaputra rivers. The most important feature of the region is the extensive flooding by rivers and by rain water. Rainfall occurs mostly in the summer and ranges between 2 000 and 4 000 mm.

The soils are mainly Eutric and Calcaric Fluvisols. The Calcaric Fluvisols occur only in the calcareous alluvium of the Ganges river. The material deposited by the Brahmaputra is noncalcareous and forms Eutric Fluvisols.

The soil pattern consists of river levees and basins, with loamy soils which are sandy in spots, and clay soils respectively. While the clay soils are flooded quite deeply during the summer rainy season, the loamy soils are generally flooded with shallow water and drain quite quickly in the autumn at the end of the rainy season. The drainage condition of the soils is the most important factor affecting land use.

The Nitosols covering a small area in the centre of the region represent an old surface of an uplifted block of clay, probably of Pleistocene or Tertiary age (FAO, 1971b). In the south there is an area of Dystric Histosols formed in fresh water swamps; in some places they have a thin clay cover. Thionic Fluvisols occur along the coast in a belt about 30 to 40 km wide, and are covered by mangrove forest.

16. *Cambisols of Burma, Bangladesh and India*

The major part of this region is hilly with elevations ranging from 1 000 to 3 000 metres. The climate is humid tropical with precipitation ranging from 2 000 to 5 000 mm per annum. The vegetation comprises tropical evergreen and deciduous forests.

The soil pattern is influenced mainly by topography and altitude. In the north the undulating areas have Orthic and Ferric Acrisols as well as Dystric Nitosols. In the hilly area in the centre and northeast, where the altitude is more than 1 000 metres, the main soils are Humic Cambisols. The southwestern hilly part, with lower elevations, has Dystric Cambisols. Along the coast there are Eutric Gleysols. The Brahmaputra flood plain in the north has a strip of Eutric Fluvisols. A part of the Irrawaddy flood plain in the northeast also has Eutric Fluvisols.

17. *Acrisol-Fluvisol association of the Irrawaddy basin in Burma*

Extending from the coast in the south to the centre of Burma in the north, this region occupies a 150-to 200-km-wide belt. Most of the area is undulating to rolling or nearly level, with elevations ranging between a few metres and 500 metres above sea level. The climate is tropical to subtropical subhumid, with 750 to 2 500 mm rainfall, except for a small part in the north, which receives only 500 to 750 mm. The natural vegetation, comprising tropical evergreen and deciduous forest, has deteriorated in many parts of the region.

The main soils are Acrisols and Luvisols in the undulating to rolling and hilly areas and Eutric Fluvisols in the nearly level flood plains of the rivers. Ferric Acrisols occur in the south, whereas the northern undulating part has Chromic Luvisols. The Acrisols and Luvisols have developed on peneplains of Tertiary calcareous shale and sandstone, which occur with some metamorphic gneiss as well as basalt and granite. The Eutric Fluvisols occurring in the flood plains of the Irrawaddy and Sittang rivers cover about one third of this region. The delta area in the south has mainly Eutric Gleysols and the land subject to sea flooding has Gleyic Solonchaks.

18. *Nitosol-Acrisol association of eastern Burma*

This soil region covers the Shan plateau, an old and stable land mass which is considered part of the Indian shield. Most of the land surface represents an old peneplain. Elevations range from 500 to 1 500 metres. The climate is humid tropical in the south and subhumid in the north. The rocks are gneiss, schist, slate and granite as well as some shale and siltstone.

The soils are mainly Dystric and Humic Nitosols and Orthic Acrisols. Humic Nitosols occur in the central and eastern parts of the region in high altitude areas where the forest has not been disturbed. The rest of the area is covered by Dystric Nitosols. However, in the south where the slopes are steep, shallow phases of Orthic and Ferric Acrisols occur with some associated Calcaric Cambisols.

19. *Cambisols of the Himalayas*

Covering the Himalayas and part of the Hindu Kush mountains, this soil region extends from the northeastern border of India to the northeastern part of Afghanistan. As it includes both the high mountains and the foothills, elevations vary from about 500 metres to 8 484 metres (Mount Everest in the Himalayas). The climate ranges from subtropical subhumid to humid in the foothills, to temperate subhumid to humid in the mountains. Precipitation ranges between 1 200 mm and 2 000 mm in most of the region, and in the east is more than 2 500 mm. However, beyond the high ranges it decreases rapidly, especially in the northwestern part, the northernmost sector of which receives only about 100 mm.

The main rocks are gneiss, schist and slate in the high range core of the Himalayas, and Tertiary calcareous shale, sandstone and limestone in the middle and low ranges. The foothills comprise calcareous shale, sandstone and conglomerates, all semiconsolidated. The slopes are steep and valleys are deeply entrenched. The area north of the highest ranges forms a high plateau.

The main soils are Dystric Cambisols, Lithosols and Dystric Regosols, in addition to a narrow strip of Dystric Regosols along the India-Nepal border. The Cambisols occur on the low parts of slopes, on old river terraces, and in lacustrine and loess deposits. The lacustrine deposits are found in the Katmandu valley and other mountain valleys, whereas loess deposits are quite extensive in some valleys in the western part of the region. Associated with the Cambisols are some Orthic Luvisols. The Regosols occur on gravelly or stony colluvial deposits on steep slopes. Lithosols, which occupy the upper parts of the hill slopes, account for the major part of the area. Areas lying above 7 000 metres are covered by perennial snow caps.

References

AHMAD, M. *et al. Reconnaissance soil survey of Thal north.*
1968 Rome, FAO. FAO/UNDP Soil Survey Project, Pakistan.

ALTAIE, F.H. *The soils of Iraq.* Ghent, State University of
1968 Ghent. (Thesis) (Mimeographed)

BOWEN-JONES, H. *et al. Survey of soils and agricultural po-*
1967 *tential in the Trucial States.* Durham, University of
Durham, Department of Geography.

BURINGH, P. *Soils and soil conditions in Iraq.* Baghdad,
1960 Ministry of Agriculture.

DAN, J. *et al. The soils and soil associations map of Israel.*
1962 Jerusalem, Ministry of Agriculture and Hebrew University of Jerusalem.

DEWAN, M.L. & FAMOURI, J. *The soils of Iran.* Rome,
1964 FAO. FAO and Soil Institute of Iran.

ELC & AB VAN KHAK. *Karkheh river basin development*
1971 *master plan*, Vol. 2. *Reconnaissance soil, land classification and land use maps,* p. 3-12. Tehran. Report
by ELC Electroconsult of Milan and Ab van Khak
of Tehran for the Government of Iran.

FAO. *Report to the Government of Nepal on soil survey inves-*
1965 *tigations and soil analysis.* Rome. FAO/EPTA Report
No. 2043.

FAO. *Survey of land and water resources, Afghanistan.* Vol. 4,
1965 *Soils.* Rome. FAO/SF Project No. 9.

FAO. Soil resources in West Pakistan. *Soil Survey Project,*
1971a *Pakistan. Technical Report 1.* Rome.

FAO. Soil Resources of East Pakistan. *Soil Survey Project,*
1971b *Pakistan. Technical Report 3.*

FAO. *Soil survey and water management research and dem-*
1971c *onstration in the Rajasthan canal area, India. Soil
survey and land classification. 1.6 Semi-detailed soil
survey of West Phase II area. 1.7 Semi-detailed soil
survey of Lunkaran lift area.* Rome.

FINIELZ, C.I. *A soils study. Classification and utilization*
1955 *with respect to irrigation in the Wadi Jizan area. Summary report.* Rome, FAO.

HARADINE, F. & COOVER, J.R. *A note on the study of some*
1967 *important Indian soils.* Rome, FAO. (Mimeographed)

MOORMANN, F.R. & PANABOKKE, C.R. *Soils of Ceylon.*
1961 Colombo, Government Press. FAO and Land Use
Division, Department of Agriculture.

OSMAN. *Contribution à l'étude des sols du Liban nord.* Gand,
1971 Université de l'Etat à Gand. (Mimeographed)

PASEUR, J.E. *A note on the soil units of the soil map of Arabia.*
1971 Rome, FAO. (Mimeographed)

RAYCHAUDHURI, S.P. *et al. Soils of India.* New Delhi,
1963 Indian Council of Agricultural Research.

ROZANOV, B.G. *Explanatory note to the soil map of Burma.*
1959 Rangoon, Land Use Bureau. (Mimeographed)

SANDERS, A.F. *et al. The reconnaissance soil survey of Sarakhs*
1968 *area, Khorasan, Iran.* Rome, FAO; Tehran, Soil Institute
of Iran.

SHAMOOT, S.A. & HUSSINI, K. *Land and water use in the*
1969 *Hashemite Kingdom of Jordan. Part I, Land resources.*
A paper submitted to the Near East Land and Water
Use Meeting held in Amman, Jordan in May 1969.
Amman, Al Hurieh.

SMITH, R. *Report on the soils of Yemen highlands.* Type-
1970 script. Rome, FAO. (Mimeographed)

SUBRAMANIAN, V.S. *et al. Survey of land and water resources,*
1963 *Afghanistan.* Vol. 4, *Soils.* Rome, FAO.

TESCO/FAO. *Summary of the agricultural potential of Wadi*
1971 *Zabid. Soils and land capability. Yemen Arab Republic.* Report by TESCO, VIZITERV-VITUKI, Budapest,
for FAO, Rome.

VAN LIERE, W.J. *Report to the Government of Syria on the*
1965 *classification and rational utilization of soils.* Rome,
FAO. FAO/EPTA Report No. 2075.

VEENENBOS, J.S. *Unified report of the soil and land classifi-*
1968 *cation of Dezful project, Khuzistan, Iran.* Rome, FAO;
Tehran, Soil Institute of Iran,

VERHEYE, W. *Formation, classification and land evaluation of*
1972 *soils in Mediterranean areas, with special reference to
the southern Lebanon.* Ghent, State University of
Ghent. (Thesis) (Mimeographed)

6. LAND USE AND SOIL SUITABILITY

The land use of an area depends upon soil, climate, hydrological characteristics and prevalent socio-economic conditions. Thus the soil is only one of the factors that influence land use, though in many cases it becomes the determining factor. For example, vegetable crops cannot be grown on stony Regosols or Plinthic Acrisols, and fruit orchards or tree crops cannot be raised on Vertisols. In other cases, however, climate, hydrology or socio-economic factors may be more important than the soil. In South Asia vast desert areas are used mainly for poor grazing because of very low rainfall. Likewise, very cold areas in the high mountains are of little use owing to the low temperatures. In the Ganges delta in Bangladesh most of the land is so severely flooded in summer that only rice can be grown. Subsistence agriculture is prevalent in large areas of South Asia because farmers are illiterate and often too poor to buy fertilizers, insecticides and improved implements.

Extending from Burma, India and Sri Lanka in the east to Syria, Lebanon and Saudi Arabia in the west, the region of South Asia has been inhabited since ancient times. Land use evolved according to the soil conditions, climate, hydrology, available skills and economic considerations. The population densities therefore adjusted according to what the land could produce under prevalent conditions. Population distribution in South Asia ranges from very dense (Bangladesh) to very sparse (Saudi Arabia). In Bangladesh the Ganges flood plain has fertile Fluvisols which, aided by heavy rainfall, flooding and high temperatures, can produce two to three rice crops a year. Hence population density has reached a level of more than 300 persons per square kilometre. However, in Saudi Arabia the desertic conditions have never allowed the population to increase to more than 10 persons per square kilometre.

In many areas the original conditions have changed during the last two decades. New irrigation schemes have been put into operation either to cultivate new areas or to make crop production secure in cultivated areas. For example, in some areas in Israel irrigation has changed the cropping pattern from small grains to a mixed farming which includes fruit orchards, livestock and poultry in addition to cereal crops. In Jordan and Saudi Arabia some desert areas have been put under irrigation with tube-wells making use of an extensive sandstone aquifer. New technologies are being adopted, making it possible to increase crop yields by more than 100%. Thus, it can be expected that major changes in land use will take place at least in some areas. For example, forage production and fruit orchards may replace cereal production in the mountain regions of Syria and Pakistan.

The ecological conditions of South Asia vary greatly, so land use varies accordingly from production of tropical fruits and commercial crops (tea, coconut, coffee, and others) to extensive poor grazing and to the production of temperate fruits. The main types of land use are described briefly below. More details are given later under each soil unit.

In high rainfall areas such as Burma, Sri Lanka, eastern and southeastern parts of India and the Caspian coast in Iran, rice is the main crop. It is grown mostly with rain water or flood water from the rivers. In many places more than one crop is grown a year. Very little manuring is done; a little dung manure is added once every three or four years. In the winter a large part of the area is put under a fodder legume, khesari (*Lathyrus sativa*), and gram (*Cicer arietinum*). Mustard is another important winter crop. Soil fertility is maintained by the legumes as well as by fresh silt sediments and weathering of minerals in the soil.

In the many hilly areas in Burma, Sri Lanka and northeastern India a system of shifting cultivation is practised, with upland rice as the main crop. The forest is cleared by cutting and burning to grow crops for a few years. Then the land is abandoned owing to depleted fertility and cultivation is shifted to a new area.

In the humid tropical areas tea, coffee, coconut, rubber and spices are quite important crops. Coconut and rubber trees are grown on low plains, coffee in the low hills and tea on high hills.

In the Mesopotamian and Indus plains agriculture is mainly dependent upon canal irrigation. A large part of the Ganges flood plain is also irrigated by canals. In the Indus and Ganges plains many different crops are grown. Cotton, sugarcane, wheat, rice, millet, maize, pulses, mustard and fodder legumes are the main crops. Paddy is grown in the poorly drained basin areas of the Indus delta and the eastern Ganges plain. In the Mesopotamian plain irrigated dates, wheat and barley are the main crops. Rice is grown only in basin areas or at edges of swamps. The date orchards are quite well managed, with dung manure being applied almost every year, but wheat and barley are raised without much care and without fertilizer. The production of forage crops is practically unknown; fodder legumes have been introduced only recently.

In the Mesopotamian and Indus plains the water supply is limited in relation to the extensive areas of good land. Hence cropping intensities are low, a large percentage of the area remaining fallow. Low-intensity cropping has helped to postpone the drainage problem, but a stage has now been reached where it is necessary to provide drainage to control salinity and the high water table. In Pakistan tube-wells are being used in some areas to lower the water table. At present the tube-wells are being installed only in areas in which the ground water is not highly saline and can be used to supplement the canal supplies. A few surface drains have been made to dispose of excess storm water. In Iraq an elaborate system of tile and open drains is being installed in some areas. For controlling the salinity problem a change from traditional to intensive cropping is essential, so that land remains under crops most of the time and the salt and water movements are kept on a downward course.

Wells are also an important source of irrigation in northern India and in Maharashtra, Tamil Nadu and Rajasthan states. Irrigation from rain water "tanks"[1] is quite important in southern India, in some parts of northern India, and in Sri Lanka. Irrigation from wells is also important in the northern part of the Indus plains in Pakistan.

In the subhumid and semiarid areas rainfed cropping of wheat, barley and millet is the main land use. In central India millet covers most of the cultivated land in the summer. Under higher rainfall cotton is an important crop. During winter pulses and oilseed crops are grown. Wheat and barley are the main crops in the semiarid areas of the Near East (northeastern Iraq through northern Syria to Lebanon, Jordan and Israel). The land is kept fallow for a year and wheat or barley is grown

the following year. This cropping pattern is changed only where irrigation is introduced, as in Israel.

In the arid areas, grazing of goats, sheep and cattle is the main land use. Such areas cover major parts of Saudi Arabia, Iraq, Syria, Jordan, Iran, Afghanistan, Pakistan and western India. There is no control on the use of grazing land and overgrazing is prevalent everywhere except in areas which are far from water sources. In the southwestern part of the Arabian Peninsula, however, well-managed community pastures have existed since at least the early Islamic period.

In the arid mountain valleys a system of underground irrigation channels is used by which the ground water in the gravelly fans is brought to the valley bottom through a tunnel interconnecting a series of wells. These channels are called "karezes" in Pakistan, "ghanats" in Iran and "fuggaras" in Jordan. The water flows by force of gravity and is utilized for irrigation of wheat and some fruits and vegetables. In some areas this irrigation system is being replaced by tube-wells operated by diesel engines or electricity.

Torrent-watered wheat is grown in some arid mountain valleys and piedmont plains. The crop is neither truly rainfed nor irrigated, and production varies a great deal from year to year as the rains are quite uncertain. During the short flash floods the water of hill torrents is diverted by low earth dams built across the streams and taken through channels to fields which have high embankments for deep flooding.

Land use by soil units is discussed in more detail as follows. The soil units are arranged in alphabetical order of symbols.

A. Acrisols

Af. FERRIC ACRISOLS

Use. These soils occur mainly in northeastern India and southern and western Burma. The relief is undulating to rolling. In both countries these soils are mostly under forest. In India some areas are used for growing rice and potato crops under shifting cultivation. In Burma small areas are used for growing poor crops of rice, sorghum and sesame.

Suitability. Having reached an advanced stage of weathering, these soils are highly acid, low in bases as well as phosphate. Nevertheless, they have good physical properties and are quite suitable for tea, rubber and cocoa plantations, though less so than Humic Acrisols. Pineapples and other tropical fruits also do quite well, but require heavy applications of phosphate, potassium and nitrogen fertilizers.

---

[1] Earthen structures made by building embankments around a dug-out area. They are used to store rain water to be used for irrigation during dry spells between rains.

Rice and sugarcane can be grown, but for sustained high yields special management including the use of complete fertilizers and lime is needed. Sloping areas are better left under forest.

Ag. GLEYIC ACRISOLS

See Lg. Gleyic Luvisols.

Ah and Ao. HUMIC AND ORTHIC ACRISOLS

Use. These soils occur in humid tropical areas in southwestern and northeastern India, the central part of Sri Lanka, and small areas in Bangladesh. They occupy well-drained hill sites and form good land for rubber plantations and fruit orchards. In Burma they are mainly under bamboo and shrub as a result of the destruction of forest during shifting cultivation. Some areas are under rubber plantations or fruit orchards. In Sri Lanka they are mostly under forest, but they also support the best cocoa plantations as well as tea, coconut and rubber plantations and fruit orchards. Vegetables and tobacco are produced in a special rain shadow area. In low rainfall areas settled agriculture is found only where a source of irrigation water exists.

In India these soils are used for growing poor crops of millet, pulses and mustard. In Kerala state plantations of tea, rubber, coconut and areca nut are raised on Humic Acrisols. In a few places they are terraced for rice cultivation. The shallow soils are used only for grazing. In northeastern India (Assam state) they are used for shifting cultivation, with rice as the main crop. Some areas are under tea plantations. Oilseed crops, millet and some cotton are often intersown with rice. Fruit trees, bananas, vegetables and tobacco are grown around homesteads.

Suitability. Having reached an advanced stage of weathering, these soils have a low natural fertility and are especially low in phosphate. Application of phosphate, nitrogen, potassium and sometimes lime is required for sustained high production of appropriate crops. Under a suitable climate they are good soils for tea, coffee, rubber and tropical fruits. In sloping areas terracing is needed to check erosion. Shifting cultivation creates serious erosion problems and should be replaced by settled agriculture to check further damage to the soil. Areas occupying high sites are well to somewhat excessively drained and often suffer from drought, as in Burma and Bangladesh. In such cases, the provision of irrigation by tube-wells can greatly improve crop production.

Ap and Lp. PLINTHIC ACRISOLS AND PLINTHIC LUVISOLS

In India these soils occur in areas near the east coast and in the south near the west coast. They also occupy some areas in Sri Lanka and foothills in Burma. As they are remnants of an ancient eroded surface, they have iron concretions at or near the surface. They are either under scrub forest or grasses and are used for some grazing. They are generally not suitable for agriculture and may be left under permanent vegetation. Under special management including the use of complete fertilizers and lime, some areas may be used for production of sorghum, maize, groundnuts and fruits.

B. Cambisols

Bc. CHROMIC CAMBISOLS

Use. These soils occur mainly in areas under a subhumid climate in eastern and southern India and in small areas in Burma. They are used for growing rain-fed crops of millet, sorghum, sesame, mustard and castor beans. In eastern India barley is also an important crop. Rice is grown wherever supplemental irrigation is available.

Suitability. Low rainfall, low fertility and erosion limit suitability for agriculture. These soils can produce good crops only if irrigation and fertilizers are provided and proper soil conservation measures are taken. Millet, sesame, linseed and tur (*Cajanus indicus*) grow without irrigation. Rice, cotton, sugarcane and tropical fruits would grow well with irrigation.

Bd. DYSTRIC CAMBISOLS

Use. These soils occur mainly in the high rainfall areas of the Himalayas in India, Nepal, Bhutan and Pakistan, and in Bangladesh. They also occur in Syria, Lebanon, northern Iran and western Burma. They usually occupy moderate to steep slopes and are mainly under forest or are used for grazing. A small part of such areas is terraced to grow irrigated rice or rainfed maize, wheat, potatoes and fruits such as apples and pears. In Iran, Bangladesh and northeastern India (Assam and West Bengal) some areas with these soils are used for tea plantations. At altitudes exceeding 3 000 metres (as in Nepal) barley and wheat are the main crops. Maize and millet are grown up to 3 000 metres while potatoes are produced up to 4 000 metres.

Suitability. Owing to the steepness of slopes, these soils are subject to severe erosion unless properly terraced. They are suitable for forests and controlled grazing. With intensive soil conservation measures such as bench terracing they can be used for growing apples, pears, potatoes, maize and wheat. With irrigation from springs, rice can be grown up to 2 000 metres altitude. Sandy clay loam and loamy soils with good internal drainage are among the best soils for tea.

These soils are poor in plant food, especially phosphate and bases. For sustained high crop yields they require application of potassium, nitrogen, lime and phosphate. As the organic matter content is sufficient for good physical condition, these soils respond well to the application of fertilizers and other good management practices.

Be, Bk and Bv. EUTRIC, CALCIC AND VERTIC CAMBISOLS

Use. These soils occur in subhumid to semiarid climates and are used for rainfed cultivation of wheat, sorghum and barley, usually followed by a year of fallow. In Burma these soils are used for rice in low-lying areas and for maize, sorghum and sesame on moderately well-drained sites. Chillies, groundnuts and beans are also grown on well-drained soils. The irrigated parts are used for growing rice, vegetables and maize. Irrigation is being introduced in some new areas. In some parts of Pakistan sugarcane, tobacco, fruits, maize, wheat and fodder crops are grown under canal irrigation. In the rainfed area wheat is the main crop grown after a year of fallow, and is followed immediately by sorghum. During the fallow period the land is grazed in winter but ploughed up after every rain in summer to conserve rain moisture for the wheat crop. In some areas considerable quantities of groundnuts are grown, especially on loamy soils. In India and Sri Lanka they are used mainly for growing sugarcane, groundnuts, maize, sesame and chillies, and in low-lying parts for rice. In Gujarat and Maharashtra states (India) the main rainfed crops are millet, paddy, groundnuts, wheat and castor beans. Under irrigation rice, sugarcane, cotton, wheat and sorghum are grown. In the Ganges plain these soils are mainly under irrigated wheat, rice, sugarcane, pulses and fodder crops.

With or without irrigation, rice is the main crop in the mountainous tract of India and Nepal. In the eastern part of this tract sometimes two crops of paddy are grown a year. In the western part, in Kashmir and in some areas of Pakistan, maize is the main crop, together with irrigated rice and potatoes. In Assam state in northeastern India some hilly areas of Eutric Cambisols are under tea planta-

tions. In Nepal jute and sugarcane are also grown. In the hilly areas at higher altitudes apples and maize are grown with irrigation. Wheat is grown up to 4 000 metres altitude and barley up to 5 000 metres. In Nepal and India shifting cultivation is practised in some areas by hill tribes. The land is cleared of forest by cutting and burning. After the land is hoed, the seed is dibbled in or broadcast. The main crops are rice, millet and oilseeds. After two or three years of cultivation the land is left fallow and a new area is cultivated. This practice has caused deterioration of the forest and severe soil erosion. In Lebanon olives, grapes and wheat are grown without irrigation, whereas apple, citrus and vegetable crops are irrigated.

In Iran, Calcic Cambisols on the northern slopes of the Elburz mountains are used mainly for rice while some Eutric Cambisols at high altitudes are under tea plantations. Pistachio and almond are the important crops carried by Calcic Cambisols on the southern slopes of the Elburz and Zagros mountains and the mountain area of the central Iranian plateau.

Suitability. These soils constitute good agricultural land except in steep topography. Water erosion and moisture shortage due to inadequate rainfall are the main problems. Supplemental irrigation is necessary for obtaining high crop yields in areas that do not have high rainfall. In intermontane valleys in the Himalayas rainfall is usually sufficient for good crops of maize and wheat, the only limiting factor being the low temperature in the winter. They are quite fertile soils, and need only nitrogen and phosphorus to produce high crop yields. Potassium is needed where nitrogen and phosphorus have been in use for a number of years. Organic matter is usually sufficient and the soils are easily worked to good tilth. With supplemental irrigation many crops can be grown, according to the climate.

In the hilly areas all Cambisols are suitable for the production of temperate fruits such as apples; Eutric Cambisols are also very good soils for tea cultivation. In rainfed subhumid areas with summer rainfall (e.g. Pakistan) crop production can be increased by introducing some legumes in the fallow period, or by shifting to summer crops; for instance, groundnuts on loamy soils and sorghum on clay soils instead of wheat. However, phosphate application is necessary for sustained production of groundnuts and other legumes.

Water erosion is a serious problem and proper soil conservation measures are needed to check it. Shifting cultivation on hills is very damaging and must be discouraged by persuading the farmers to adopt settled agriculture. Permanent agriculture should be limited to deep soils on moderate slopes. All steep land with shallow soils should remain under forest or be reverted to forest.

Bf. Ferralic Cambisols

Use. These soils occur in association with Nitosols in small areas in western India and Burma. The topography is undulating to rolling. They are used for millet, wheat and linseed. Some areas are under scrub forest.

Suitability. These soils have low fertility and are especially low in phosphate. Because of undulating or rolling topography they also suffer from erosion and drought. They are suitable for growing millet and wheat. With proper soil conservation measures, such as terracing, and adequate application of fertilizer they can produce good crops.

Bh. Humic Cambisols

Use. Humic Cambisols occur mainly in the Terai plain at the foot of the Himalayas in India, Nepal and Bangladesh and in some areas in western Burma. They are little used for agriculture and mainly remain under forest. Rice is the principal crop in areas where the forest has been cleared (e.g. in northern Bangladesh), and there is some tea cultivation in northern India.

Suitability. These soils are often rather sandy and have rapid permeability. This poses limitations for rice cultivation in years of below-average rainfall and calls for provision of supplemental irrigation. Drainage for cultivation of dryland crops in the monsoon season might be practicable, but irrigation of such crops in the dry season might require excessive applications of water. They may also require special fertilizer treatments, especially if used for such crops as sugarcane or legumes.

D and P. Podzoluvisols and Podzols

Use. Dystric and Eutric Podzoluvisols and Humic Podzols occupy small areas in the Himalayas in Nepal, Bhutan and India. They are mainly under conifer forests. Only a few small areas are terraced and used for growing maize, potatoes, wheat and temperate fruits.

Suitability. Because of hilly relief these soils are best suited for forests. Proper bench terracing is essential for the cultivation of crops. Application of lime, phosphate and potassium is also needed for obtaining good crop yields. Tropical fruits, potatoes and maize are suitable crops.

E. Rendzinas

Use. These soils occur as inclusions in Lithosol areas in Lebanon, Syria, Iraq, Israel and Jordan. Because of shallow depth and the very high lime content in the subsoil, these soils are droughty and present fertility problems. They are used mainly for scrub forest or grazing. In some areas they are used for olives and figs, both rainfed and irrigated. Some rainfed wheat and barley are also grown. In Lebanon and Israel they are being developed for irrigated vegetable gardens, fruit orchards and vineyards.

Suitability. Rendzinas are mainly suitable for forest and grazing. High-value crops of vegetables and fruits grown with irrigation require special management. Only olives, figs, grapes, wheat, barley and alfalfa can withstand the high lime content of these soils. Intensive research is in progress in Lebanon on their use and management problems.

F. Ferralsols

Use. These soils occur only to a minor extent in India, Nepal, Burma and Sri Lanka. Rhodic Ferralsols occurring in the dry zone of Sri Lanka are little used, even under shifting cultivation. In the 1 500- to 2 000-mm rainfall zone some Ferralsols are used for growing coconut. In Nepal, India and Burma they are mainly under forest, but some areas are used for barley, millet and oilseed crops.

Suitability. Low fertility and low moisture-holding capacity are the major limitations. These soils are deep and permeable, however, and where irrigation can be provided they are suitable for tree crops. Heavy use of phosphate and nitrogen fertilizers would be required, and minor element deficiencies might show up under intensive cultivation. Wherever better soils are available, Ferralsols may be left under forest.

G. Gleysols

Gc, Gd and Ge. Calcaric, Dystric and Eutric Gleysols

Use. Large and contiguous areas of these soils occur only in Burma, Bangladesh and Iran, but small patches are found in almost all river valleys. Poor drainage restricts land use and potential on all great groups of the Gleysols. The Eutric Gleysols [2] are

---

[2] Dystric Gleysols also occur and have similar use and potential.

widely developed on piedmont and low terrace sites in Bangladesh. They are mainly used for cultivation of rice and a little jute or mesta (kenaf). Trees are rare except around homesteads, and dryland crops are rarely grown. In the more humid eastern and central parts of Bangladesh the soils are mainly double-cropped: an early broadcast rice crop (aus) is followed by a late transplanted rice crop (aman). In the drier Barind tract, which extends into India, the main transplanted aman crop is preceded by aus broadcast on a small proportion of the land which varies each year according to the incidence of pre-monsoon rainfall.

Irrigated rice is the main crop on Gleysols on the Caspian coast in northern Iran. Calcaric Gleysols in Pakistan are mainly basin clays used for irrigated rice and wheat. The small patches of Calcaric Gleysols in the arid and semiarid valleys are mainly used for grazing, as in Afghanistan. In Iraq some areas are under rice cultivation. Marshland is often used for grazing buffaloes.

Suitability. These soils are best adapted to rice cultivation where rainfall is adequate or irrigation can be provided. Cultivation of dryland crops is generally impossible with or without irrigation because of the drainage problem and the prominent plough pan which these soils generally develop under rice cultivation. With irrigation, two rice crops per year can be grown. Special attention to puddling is needed on light-textured soils and on clay soils that have rapid subsoil permeability. Natural fertility is generally low, and relatively heavy use of fertilizers (mainly nitrogen and phosphate) is needed to sustain high yields. In areas of high rainfall it is advisable to drain these soils for cropping, as demonstrated in an area of Humic Gleysols in Sri Lanka. In arid and semiarid areas Gleysols should be left alone because they need intensive drainage, and a lot of better land is available for development at lower cost.

Gh. HUMIC GLEYSOLS

Use. These soils occur in association with Humic Cambisols in the foothills of the Himalayas in India and Nepal, and in some areas in Sri Lanka. They are mainly under swamp [forest. Some areas of Mollic Gleysols also occur in a similar environment and have the same use. Only small areas are used for growing late rice in India and Nepal and vegetables in Sri Lanka.

Suitability. As these soils are difficult to drain, they are suitable mainly for forests. Provision of drainage for rice cultivation may be feasible, but

good crops can be raised only with special management including the application of lime and fertilizers. Deficiencies of some minor elements would also need to be corrected. It might be economic to drain some parts for vegetable production, as demonstrated in Sri Lanka.

H and K. Phaeozems and Kastanozems

Use. Haplic Phaeozems and Haplic Kastanozems occupy only minor areas in the mountainous northern parts of Iraq, Iran and India. They are mainly used for rainfed wheat and barley, but good crops of irrigated cotton are also produced in Iran. Forest and grazing land occupy uncultivated areas. Some areas in India are used for tea plantations and rice cultivation.

Suitability. These soils are suitable for agriculture if they are sufficiently deep and extensive, and require irrigation only to supplement the uncertain rainfall. Some areas of Phaeozems also need drainage.

I. Lithosols

Use. These soils occur in areas with climates ranging from arid to humid, and land use varies widely. Few are cultivated because of their shallowness, stoniness, rockiness and, sometimes, their inaccessibility. In semiarid and subhumid areas between Pakistan and the Mediterranean coast they are mainly used for grazing nomadic herds of camels, sheep and goats. In humid areas Lithosols usually occur under forest, except at very high altitude in the Himalayas. Where cultivation is practised, poor crops of upland rice, millet, sorghum, wheat, barley, " famine " millet and mustard are grown, sometimes in mixed culture, and often by hand cultivation methods.

Suitability. Since they are very shallow, Lithosols are fundamentally poor soils with little potential for improved agricultural production. They suffer widely from erosion, including wind erosion in arid areas. Stoniness, rock outcrops, and often steep slopes generally make them unsuitable for plough cultivation or irrigation. With great labour, terraces can be constructed in some humid areas which may allow arable crops to be grown satisfactorily, or even tree crops where the underlying rock is sufficiently broken to allow deep root penetration. Wherever possible, these soils are best left or put under forest, with or without strictly controlled grazing to encourage absorption of rainfall and check runoff on to adjoining land. Only patches of deep soils occurring within the Lithosol area can be used for fruit orchards where irrigation water is available from springs, as in Lebanon and Syria.

J. Fluvisols

Je, Jc and Jd. EUTRIC, CALCARIC AND DYSTRIC FLUVISOLS

Use. These three units of Fluvisols are discussed together because periodic flooding or waterlogging provides a common factor strongly determining their use and potential. Eutric and Calcaric Fluvisols are the dominant soils in the Ganges-Brahmaputra delta and on the lower portions of the adjoining flood plains. Calcaric Fluvisols are particularly associated with Ganges alluvium. They also occur along the active flood plains of major rivers such as the Indus, Tigris and Euphrates, but other soils occupy major proportions of these river flood plains. Dystric Fluvisols are of minor importance within this region.

Eutric and Calcaric Fluvisols are among the most intensively cultivated and highly productive soils in the region. On the extensive meander flood plains and the Ganges-Brahmaputra delta, cropping patterns are related to landscape position. The higher, more permeable ridge soils which are subject to flooding for short periods are commonly used for an early broadcast aus rice crop followed by mustard, pulses fodder legumes or sweet potatoes sown from September through October. Jute and sugarcane are sometimes grown on this land as well, and sugar palm (*Phoenix silvestris*) is particularly associated with calcareous levee soils. Around homesteads many different crops are grown: domestic vegetables, spices, tobacco, betel leaf, betel nut and various fruit trees, especially mango. On less permeable soils subject to flooding less than about 90 cm deep, broadcast aus rice is followed by late transplanted aman rice harvested in December. Jute is substituted for aus rice on up to about 40% of the land. The transplanted aman is sometimes followed by dry season crops, usually low-quality fodder legumes such as khesari. However, much of the land remains fallow in the dry season.

On land flooded about 1 to 2 metres deep, aus rice is commonly sown mixed with deep-water aman rice; the aus is harvested as the flood water rises in June through July while the aman continues to grow for harvesting in November. This practice provides the farmer with a form of insurance against the loss of one or the other of the rice crops due to early or rapid flooding. Jute is also commonly grown on such land, sometimes mixed with deep-water aman. The deep-water aman is followed by dry season

crops such as mustard, rapeseed, black gram (*Cicer arietinum*) and khesari. The khesari is often sown before the rice crop is harvested, whereas other crops such as wheat, barley, linseed, lentils, black gram, onions and garlic are sown after the rice is harvested, as are potatoes and chillies which are usually irrigated from simple low-lift devices. Much of this land is in continuous production throughout the year and remains productive despite the little manuring practised.

On land flooded more than about 2 metres deep, deep-water aman paddy (which can extend its stem to as much as 6 metres where necessary) is usually the only crop grown, but it is sometimes followed by a poor fodder crop, usually khesari. Despite the great depth of flooding, jute is sometimes grown on this land, and must be harvested by diving from boats. Deep-water aman paddy is often subject to damage or loss by a too-early or too-rapid rise in flood levels. Where this hazard is too great, and where enough water can be kept on the land after flooding or can be provided by irrigation, a transplanted rice crop (boro) is grown in the winter dry season. There has been a huge expansion of winter rice cultivation in recent years with the introduction of thousands of small portable diesel pumps.

In Burma these soils are used mainly for rice, although some better-drained loamy soils are used for vegetables, groundnuts, maize and sesame. In Sri Lanka rice is the main crop and coconut is grown on better-drained sites.

On the active flood plains of the Indus and its tributaries Calcaric Fluvisols are used only for winter cropping on residual moisture provided by summer floods. The main crops are wheat, gram, mustard, rape and some lentils. Crop yields are usually low owing to moisture shortage at the time of crop maturity. In recent years tube-wells have been installed in some places to provide supplemental irrigation, mainly for wheat. After completion of the Tarbela dam on the Indus river the incidence of flooding will decrease, and the use of tube-well irrigation is expected to become quite common.

On the active flood plain of the Euphrates, Calcaric Fluvisols are used for vegetable production in the summer after the floods have receded. In the part of the lower Mesopotamian plain where there is no flooding, they are used for irrigated dates, barley, wheat and millet. However, large unirrigated areas are wasteland. In Iran date orchards are extensively grown on the estuary plain of the Karun river. The soils are Calcaric Fluvisols, which appear as inclusions in the Solonchak association shown on the map. Where these soils are not flooded, they may be partly used for irrigated general cropping, as in Jordan, or for irrigated wheat and barley, as in Saudi Arabia. In the southwestern part of the Arabian Peninsula some areas are used for growing torrent-watered sorghum and sesame.

Suitability. Although under traditional management crop yields are generally moderate to low, many of the Fluvisols in the Ganges-Brahmaputra delta and flood plains have maintained continuous crop production for centuries with low levels of manuring and whatever nutrients are added by sedimentation or released by weathering. Under modern management the soils respond well to fertilizer use (mainly nitrogen and phosphorus) and are capable of giving very high yields of the new IRRI rice varieties wherever irrigation is practicable in the dry season or hydrological conditions are suitable for their cultivation in the monsoon season. With modern management, better water control is the major input needed for increased production: first, irrigation, so that an additional rice crop or a high-value dryland crop can be grown in the dry season; then, on the more deeply flooded land, flood protection and drainage, so that one or two high-yielding rice crops can be grown in the monsoon season in place of the present low-yielding traditional varieties. Flood protection and drainage are generally not practicable on active flood plains, and increased yields on such land must be sought from the use of better seed, fertilizers and plant protection measures. In some areas (e.g. along the Indus) tube-wells located on high ground can be used for supplemental irrigation. After provision of irrigation, use of nitrogen and phosphate fertilizers is essential for obtaining high crop yields.

Under rice cultivation, a plough pan develops at the base of the ploughed layer and impedes drainage and root penetration. For dryland crops, especially those under irrigation, this pan needs to be broken up. Even for rice, it could advantageously be broken up and reformed at a greater depth than the present 5 to 10 cm, but this is possible only where mechanical cultivation is practised.

In irrigated areas loamy soils are suitable for a wide variety of crops adapted to the climate, but clay soils are suitable only for rice and a few other crops like wheat, millet and sugarcane. Salinity and a high water table, the major problems under irrigation, can be controlled by drainage and intensive cropping (for details, see Yermosols). Application of nitrogen and phosphate is necessary for high crop yields.

Jt. THIONIC FLUVISOLS

Use. These soils occur under mangrove forest or on land cleared of such forest. They are most extensive in the Sunderbans of the Ganges delta, but they occur widely elsewhere at the mouths of rivers debouching into the Bay of Bengal, and to a lesser extent along the west coast of India. Where brought under cultivation with the aid of protective embankments or drainage, the soils are mainly used for a single crop of transplanted rice in the monsoon season. Yields are generally low, however, and patches of soil remain bare due to toxic acidity.

Suitability. These soils are best left under forest. This not only has productive value in terms of timber and pulpwood, but also protective value for life and property inland against the ravages of the cyclones which regularly affect coastal areas of the Bay of Bengal. Reclamation of these soils for agriculture is costly and not always economically justifiable. It involves embankment against continued salt water flooding, drainage to leach salt and excess acidity after drainage, and subsequent heavy applications of lime and fertilizers to neutralize acidity and build up fertility. Prospects for irrigation are generally limited by the occurrence of these soils in areas where both ground water and surface water are saline. Where successfully reclaimed, they are suitable only for rice cultivation.

K. Kastanozems

See H. Phaeozems.

L. Luvisols

Lc and Lo. CHROMIC AND ORTHIC LUVISOLS

Use. Chromic Luvisols occur over extensive areas in Sri Lanka and southeastern India and small areas in Israel, Lebanon and Syria. Orthic Luvisols are extensive only in the Ganges plain and along the southeast coast of India. Elsewhere they occur only as minor associates with the Chromic Luvisols. Since these soils occur under climates ranging from humid to subhumid, at different altitudes, and occupy varying slopes, their use also varies accordingly. Large areas are too shallow or too steep for arable cropping and are used for grazing or forestry.

In India they are used mainly for rainfed crops of sorghum, millet, groundnuts, sesame, pulses and mustard. Rice is grown in areas where rainfall is sufficient or irrigation water is available. In Mysore, Tamil Nadu and Kerala states they are used for plantations of tea on high elevations and coffee in foothills. Cardamom, pepper, ginger and turmeric are also grown in Kerala. In Tamil Nadu some areas are under cinchona plantations. Crop yields are usually low except in well-managed plantations of commercial crops such as tea, coffee and spices.

In Sri Lanka Chromic Luvisols on high elevations are used mainly for tea plantations; the best-flavoured tea is produced in the semihumid hilly areas. Rubber is grown on Chromic and Orthic Luvisols on intermediate elevations and low plains. Coconut plantations are found mainly in the Orthic Luvisol areas of the plains. The subhumid hilly areas have long been under shifting cultivation of rice, and much damage has been done by excessive erosion. Settled agriculture is found either on a few large holdings or where water is available for irrigation. In Burma sorghum, maize, groundnuts and sugarcane are grown on these soils. Many areas once under shifting cultivation were abandoned owing to excessive erosion and are now under scrub forest.

In Israel these soils are used for irrigated citrus and other subtropical fruits, and for vegetables and groundnuts. Clay soils are used for maize, cotton and forage crops. In Syria deciduous fruits, cotton and citrus are grown. In Lebanon wheat and forage crops and some irrigated citrus are produced in the north, whereas olives, grapes, plums, apples and vegetables are grown on terraced fields in the south, often without irrigation.

Suitability. Shallowness and high susceptibility to erosion are the main limitations of these soils. They have good structure and are easily worked to good tilth. The deep soils are quite suitable for a variety of crops, including fruits and vegetables appropriate to the climate, if they are fertilized with phosphorus, nitrogen and some potassium. The Luvisols of southern India are intensively leached and may also require application of lime. The soils in the Near East are well supplied with lime, possibly owing to the calcareous dust carried by the wind during the dry period. They also need intensive soil conservation measures such as terracing to protect them from erosion on slopes. In most areas groundnuts, wheat, sorghum, pulses and oilseeds are the most suitable crops. In some areas they are very suitable for growing tea, coffee and spices. Supplemental irrigation is profitable and increases the choice of crops. On steep slopes they are better left or put under permanent vegetation, unless bench terracing is done at high cost to grow high-value crops such as tea, coffee, fruits and vegetables.

Lf. Ferric Luvisols

Use. These soils are extensive in the northeastern part of peninsular India and also occur in central Burma. Representing an advanced stage of weathering, they are high in iron oxide and low in bases. In India they are mainly used for growing rice, barley, oilseeds (mustard and rapeseed) and some pulses.

In Burma they are mainly covered by bamboo and scrub forest, but in places there are some rubber plantations and fruit gardens.

Suitability. Being low in bases and high in iron and aluminium oxides, these soils have severe deficiencies of phosphate, potassium, calcium and magnesium. Their nitrogen content is low to moderate. They are friable and have good physical properties; however, the subsoil sometimes contains appreciable quantities of iron concretions which result in a somewhat rapid permeability and a low water-holding capacity. If properly fertilized with phosphate, potassium, nitrogen and lime, they are suitable for fruit orchards and crops such as rice, groundnuts, maize, sesame and sorghum. These soils often suffer from drought, and most crops require irrigation. Rubber grows well where rainfall is sufficient or irrigation can be provided. The shallow soils are better left under forest.

Lg and Ag. Gleyic Luvisols and Gleyic Acrisols

Use. These poorly drained soils occupy small areas in Israel, Lebanon, Iran and India. In Israel they occur in depressions within the sandy " hamra " soils, and are used for irrigated fodder crops and pasture. In Lebanon they are used for olives. In India and Iran they are used mainly for rice cultivation.

Suitability. Poor drainage restricts the range of crops that can be grown on these soils, which are difficult to cultivate when wet. In Lebanon, where drainage is less restricting, irrigation is the main requirement for the expansion of crop production.

Lk. Calcic Luvisols

Use. These soils occur in India, Lebanon, Syria, Jordan and Israel. In the Near East they are used for rainfed wheat, barley, lentils, gram and sorghum. A fairly high proportion of the area is under legumes, and this practice helps to maintain soil fertility. In Israel irrigation has been introduced to grow a wide variety of field crops, fruits and forage crops. In Jordan some orchards of apples and olives have been established recently. Under rainfed conditions the main crops in India are wheat, millet and pulses; sugarcane is also grown where there is irrigation.

Suitability. Without irrigation these soils are suitable for growing wheat, barley, gram, lentils, groundnuts, sorghum and forage legumes. With irrigation and modern management including the use of complete fertilizers, they are excellent for raising a variety of fruits, vegetables and forage crops, as demonstrated in Israel. Erosion is a problem, and has been aggravated by recent mechanized cultivation in Jordan. Proper soil conservation measures are necessary to protect the soil from erosion.

Lp. PLINTHIC LUVISOLS

See Ap. Plinthic Acrisols.

N. Nitosols

Nd, Ne and Nh. DYSTRIC, EUTRIC AND HUMIC NITOSOLS

Use. These soils occupy extensive areas in the southwestern and eastern parts of India and in Sri Lanka and Burma. They are associated with Luvisols and Acrisols. As these soils occur on gentle slopes or in nearly level areas, erosion is not a serious problem. In Burma they are mainly under forest or shifting cultivation of rice, together with some pulses and oilseeds. In a few places they are used for fruit orchards. Coconut and rubber plantations are found on these soils in the humid western part of Sri Lanka. In the subhumid eastern part of the country shifting cultivation is practised with rice as the main crop, and settled agriculture is practised where ground water is available for irrigation. Irrigation from earthen rain water storage tanks is used to grow rice in a small but significant part of the area.

Along the west coast of India these soils are used for coconut, areca nut and rubber plantations as well as bananas and mangoes. In high rainfall areas rice is the main crop, as in Kerala, West Bengal, Bihar and Assam states, and sorghum and bulrush millet (*Pennisetum typhoideum*), sesame, rape, mustard and some maize are grown elsewhere. In some areas turmeric is also an important crop.

In Bangladesh Eutric Nitosols are used for poor crops of rice and mesta (*Hibiscus cannabinus* and *H. sabdariffa*) — a substitute for jute, sometimes followed by mustard and fodder legumes. Some areas are used for growing pineapples. Jackfruit trees are characteristically grown around homesteads. Shallow soils remain under forest.

Suitability. Nitosols are good deep soils on nearly level to gently undulating land and are somewhat resistant to erosion. Their main limitations are low fertility, low available phosphate content, and excessive wetness in the rainy season due to their slow permeability. Their depth makes them very suitable for tree crops and they respond well to good management. Irrigation development in areas of low rainfall pays well wherever water is available. With adequate application of complete fertilizers, especially phosphate, they can produce high crop yields. Dystric Nitosols also require application of lime. Suitable crops for these soils are those that can withstand a periodically wet subsoil due to somewhat restricted internal drainage.

O. Histosols

Use. These soils (mainly Dystric Histosols) occur in a large area in Bangladesh and are also found on the west coasts of India and Sri Lanka. They occupy basin sites which are subject to deep seasonal flooding, and remain wet throughout the dry season. They are quite extensive in the south of the Ganges flood plain, but they occur locally elsewhere in Bangladesh, especially in the Sylhet basin in the northeast. Most of them remain under natural vegetation of tall reeds and grasses, which in some areas are cut to provide material for thatching or making mats.

Rice cultivation is possible only where the soils have a mineral topsoil to provide adequate bearing capacity. Yields are generally low owing to low fertility and risk of flood damage, and probably also to physiological diseases associated with an iron-manganese imbalance which is liable to affect such highly organic soils. In India these soils are used for late rice after the rains. In Sri Lanka they lie unused, with the exception of a small area which has been developed for growing vegetables with special management.

Suitability. These soils generally have a low development potential. Not only are they affected by deep flooding, but drainage of the soils would also cause shrinkage of the organic matter and possibly irreversible hardening of the material. Where there is a mineral topsoil, increased yields are possible with the use of fertilizers and high-yielding rice varieties, but drainage should be attempted only if a high water table can be maintained through the dry season so as to keep the peat layer saturated. Where they are not subject to deep flooding, as in some areas in Sri Lanka, these soils can be developed for growing vegetables with special management including maintenance of the water table at shallow depths. In India these soils can be improved by provision of drainage for rice and other crops. Research is needed to overcome the minor element deficiencies.

P. Podzols

See D. Podzoluvisols.

Q. Arenosols

See R. Regosols.

R. and Q. Regosols and Arenosols

Use. Regosols include a wide variety of soils which, with the exception of loessial soils, generally have a restricted suitability for agricultural production because of low moisture-holding capacity. Many of them are often gravelly or stony — a limitation also common to the Arenosols. The most widespread soils are Calcaric Regosols and Cambic Arenosols occurring on gravelly or stony colluvial deposits and sand dunes in many semiarid and arid areas between the Thar desert of India and the Sinai desert bordering the Mediterranean coast. Albic Arenosols occur in Iraq and India. All these soils are mainly used for sparse grazing (and frequently overgrazing) of nomadic herds of cattle, sheep and goats. Where irrigation water is available, some — notably Calcaric Regosols on the Mediterranean coast of Israel and Lebanon — are used for citrus, groundnuts and vegetables. In the high rainfall areas bordering the coasts of India and Sri Lanka, the level or very gently undulating parts of sandy Dystric Regosol areas with fresh ground water are typically used for coconuts. Coastal sands with dune topography are of little use, however.

Calcaric Regosols on eroded loessial plains in Pakistan are used for rainfed cultivation of wheat and millet followed by a year of fallow. In Afghanistan similar loessial soils are being developed for irrigated farming.

In subhumid and humid mountain areas (Nepal, Bhutan, Iran and Syria) some gravelly Dystric and Eutric Regosols on colluvial slopes are terraced and used for growing fruits in addition to wheat, maize and some irrigated rice. However, the major part of these soils is under forest or is used for grazing. In the southwestern part of the Arabian Peninsula some areas are terraced for growing rainfed sorghum, wheat and barley.

Suitability. The sandy Regosols and Arenosols are generally poor soils because of low moisture and nutrient-holding capacity. Owing to a steep slope or a sandy nature, many Regosols have suffered considerable erosion by wind and water. Water erosion is a problem in uplands, while sandy areas are subject to wind erosion if they are not stabilized by protective vegetation. Stoniness makes cultivation difficult in colluvial soils. Under a subhumid or humid climate Eutric and Dystric Regosols are suitable for afforestation. Only under special management including heavy use of fertilizers or organic manure and provision of sprinkler irrigation can sandy Regosols and Arenosols be developed for high-yielding crop production. Elsewhere, improved pasturage can be provided in semiarid to subhumid areas by controlled grazing and, in some places, by creating stone barriers along contour ridges to reduce runoff and encourage water absorption. In arid areas only rotational grazing and adjusting use to carrying capacity can improve production. Regosols on loess are productive if rainfall is sufficient or irrigation is provided. They are low in organic matter, nitrogen and phosphate. A greatly improved crop yield can be facilitated by inclusion of a legume in crop rotation during the fallow period in subhumid areas, as in Pakistan.

S. Solonetz

Use. These soils, mostly saline-alkali Orthic Solonetz, occur extensively in northern India and in Pakistan. Although they mainly occur in irrigated areas, their formation antedates the development of irrigation. They mainly lie bare, sometimes with a sparse cover of grass or shrubs which provide scanty grazing to cattle or sheep herds. Costly attempts at reclamation have been made in parts of both India and Pakistan, so that in some areas the soils are found under crops such as rice, wheat, sorghum and berseem clover.

Suitability. In their natural state these soils have no agricultural value. Their reclamation for agricultural use is expensive and not always profitable, even where sufficient irrigation water is available to make it practicable. Reclamation requires leaching of excess salts by repeated heavy applications of irrigation water, addition of gypsum (or cultivation for a few years of strong-rooting, alkali-tolerant grasses such as *Ditlachne fusca*) to allow calcium to displace excess sodium, and provision of drainage to make leaching effective and prevent resalinization of the soils after reclamation. Many of these soils are nearly impervious and almost impossible to reclaim. Only the porous and pervious soils respond to reclamation. In areas where irrigation supplies are limited, as in Pakistan, it may be preferable to use scarce water on better soils.

T. Andosols

These soils occur in small areas in Iran. As the climate is arid, their main use is grazing and possibilities of improvement are very limited. Hilly relief impedes development with irrigation.

U. Rankers

These soils occur in the Himalayas in Pakistan, India, Nepal and Bhutan. They are mainly under forest or scrub vegetation. As they are steep and shallow, they have little suitability for cultivation, so are best left under permanent vegetation.

V. Vertisols

V and Bv. VERTISOLS AND VERTIC CAMBISOLS

Use. Vertisols occupy a vast sector of peninsular India and considerable areas in Iraq, Syria, Lebanon, Israel and Pakistan. They occur in almost all other countries of the region, but in much smaller proportion. The majority are Chromic Vertisols. Pellic Vertisols occur mainly in hydromorphic situations, usually in depression sites, and are extensive only in India. Land use varies with the climate and availability of irrigation.

In India most of the soils including associated Vertic Cambisols are under rainfed cultivation, the main crops being cotton, millet, sorghum, wheat, pulses, tobacco, groundnuts and sugarcane. The cereals are frequently grown intermixed with pulses, oilseeds (including castor and sesame in the south) and a variety of minor crops. On self-mulching soils ploughing may be done only once every three to six years, at which time deep ploughing is used to remove deep-rooting weeds. At other times, the soil is merely harrowed before crops are sown. Pellic Vertisols are sometimes used for rice in the monsoon season, but are often left fallow at this time and used only for a dry season crop, usually wheat. Where irrigation is available the main crops are sugarcane and rice, as well as wheat in northern India and sorghum or millet further south.

A small area of Vertisols in Pakistan comprises basin clays which are used mainly for irrigated rice and some winter wheat on residual moisture after rice, with or without supplemental irrigation. Some areas are used for grazing only. In Sri Lanka and Burma rice is the main crop. In Israel Vertisols are used for wheat, barley, maize, sorghum and pulses under rainfed conditions, and for sugar beet, cotton and fodder crops under irrigation. In Lebanon they are used for irrigated sugar beet, vegetables, alfalfa and wheat. In Jordan and Iraq wheat, barley, and lentils are the main crops under rainfed cultivation. Small areas are irrigated for tobacco.

Suitability. Heavy consistence and poor internal drainage (especially in Pellic Vertisols) are problems encountered in almost all Vertisol areas. Erosion is a problem in upland areas of central India. In some instances, Vertisols show salinity and alkalinity problems in the subsoil. Irrigation is generally necessary to obtain sustained high crop yields. Drainage has been provided in a part of Israel to improve rooting conditions for arable crops, and is needed in depression sites in India where irrigation is practised if crops other than rice are to be grown. These soils are not suitable for tree crops, but can be used for a wide range of arable crops, especially sugarcane, cotton, rice and the major dryland cereals. Phosphorus and nitrogen seem to be the major nutrients needed to maintain high crop yields. Ridging and shallow surface drains help improve drainage conditions and crop production. On Vertisols which are not self-mulching and have a hard, compact surface, mechanical tillage is needed for timely and proper seedbed preparation.

W. Planosols

Use. Planosols occupy small areas in Burma, Sri Lanka and India. They all have conditions of impeded internal drainage. Eutric and Solodic Planosols occurring in lowland areas of Sri Lanka are used for rice and coconuts in the wet zone and for irrigated rice in the dry zone. Large areas in the dry zone remain uncultivated and are used only for grazing. Humic Planosols occurring at elevations above 1 600 metres are little cultivated and remain under forest. In Burma they are mainly under bush forest and are used for grazing and production of firewood. Some areas are used for rice, sesame and groundnuts. Rice is the main crop in India.

Suitability. Where rainfall is adequate or irrigation can be provided, these soils are best adapted to rice cultivation.

X. Xerosols

Use. Throughout the semiarid areas of the region Haplic and Calcic Xerosols are used for poor crops of barley and wheat followed by a year of fallow during which the stubble and weeds are grazed. In drier areas barley, gram and lentils become more extensive than wheat. In hilly areas, as in Israel and the southwestern part of the Arabian Peninsula, cultivation of wheat, barley and sorghum is confined to valleys where runoff from the adjoining hills provides additional moisture. In Iraq, Syria, Lebanon and Jordan these soils form the wheat and barley belt where use of tractors has encouraged the extension of cultivation to marginal land with shallow soil or low rainfall. In Israel they are used for irrigated bananas, dates, pomegranates, cotton and winter vegetables. In western India millet, wheat, sesame and castor seed are grown in Gujarat and Rajasthan states. Irrigated wheat, sugarcane and cotton, pulses and fodder crops are grown in western India as well as in Pakistan. Rainfed wheat and gram with intercropped mustard are grown in some areas in Pakistan. In drier parts gram and barley are the main crops.

Suitability. As the Xerosols lie near the limit of rainfed agriculture, the low and sporadic rainfall makes crop production risky. Real improvement is possible only where irrigation water is available. Under rainfed conditions minor improvements can be made by including gram, lentils and other legumes in crop rotation, and using phosphate fertilizers. Introduction of legumes (lucerne) with application of phosphate fertilizer in rotation with wheat increases the wheat yield considerably in addition to providing forage for livestock (Pearson, 1970; Bilensoy, 1970). Shallow soils and sloping land should be used for grazing only.

Under canal irrigation the main problem in level plains is salinity, which develops owing to a high water table caused by lack of drainage. Proper drainage is needed to control salinity. In Pakistan tube-wells are being used to lower the water table in some areas where the ground water is not very saline and can be used by mixing it with canal water. In areas with saline ground water, as in Iraq and parts of Pakistan, a complete system of drains and intensive cropping are needed so that the movement of water and salts is downward and into the drains instead of upward, as when the soil is left fallow under conditions of a high water table and traditional cropping.

These soils are fertile and need only applications of nitrogen and phosphorus to give sustained high crop yields. The need for potassium arises only after nitrogen and phosphorus have been used for a number of years. The problem of low organic matter content can usually be overcome by combining intensive cropping with good management including adequate use of fertilizers. Calcic Xerosols and some Haplic Xerosols may present fertility problems owing to high lime content and low availability of micronutrients. This condition can be overcome to a great extent by growing only crops that can tolerate it (e.g. wheat, barley, alfalfa and figs). The problem is, however, acute in slowly permeable or shallow soils which would be better used for pasture with or without irrigation. Soils having a petrocalcic or petrogypsic horizon at shallow depth are also suitable only for grazing.

Y. Yermosols

Use. Without irrigation, these soils are normally bare or support a scanty vegetation which is grazed by nomadic herds of camel, sheep and goats. Most areas are overgrazed as the grazing is done without any system of control. The problem of overgrazing is especially serious near the animals' watering places.

In some areas in Iraq and Syria Haplic and Calcic Yermosols are used to grow a chance crop of rainfed barley that may be successful only once in three to five years. In hilly areas of the southwestern part of the Arabian Peninsula, Saudi Arabia and Jordan, wheat and barley are grown in valley bottoms and wadis where runoff from the surrounding hills collects. In the arid mountainous area of Pakistan wheat is grown in valleys under a system of flood irrigation which diverts torrent water on to the fields. However, the crop is generally marginal. In the southwestern part of the Arabian Peninsula sorghum, wheat, barley and alfalfa are grown under torrent water irrigation. Some areas are irrigated from wells to grow wheat, alfalfa and maize.

With irrigation many crops can be grown, depending on the climate. The main irrigated crops in the Indus plains in Pakistan are cotton, sugarcane, wheat, berseem clover, and on clay soils, rice. Mangoes and guavas are also grown throughout the plains in addition to oranges in the northern part of the country and bananas in the south near the sea. In high altitude areas such as Pakistan, Afghanistan, Iran and Jordan, apples and deciduous fruits and wheat are grown under irrigation from springs or from a system of underground channels which interconnect a series of wells in the mountains and bring water down to valley bottoms by force of gravity. In Israel the main irrigated crops are cotton, sugar beets, fodder crops, bananas, dates and grapes. Irrigation from tube-wells is being developed in some parts of Jordan and Saudi Arabia to utilize the water in an extensive sandstone aquifer.

Suitability. Without irrigation Yermosols are suitable only for traditional grazing. At present the vegetation is deteriorated in most areas, but in Pakistan, Saudi Arabia and Syria rotational grazing and development of additional watering places for animals have increased production from these soils. Supplemental forage must, however, be produced on a part of the adjacent irrigated areas to make the whole programme of improved management of grazing lands a success. Pastures properly managed on a community basis have existed in the southwestern part of the Arabian Peninsula since early Islamic times, and indicate how such land should be utilized without deterioration.

With the exception of the Gypsic and Calcic Yermosols, these soils are very productive when placed under irrigation and are suitable for a wide variety of crops adapted to the climate. Drainage and salinity are the main problems where large plain areas are irrigated. In small irrigated areas natural drainage by side seepage and evaporation into large unirrigated surrounding areas seem to be sufficient. In extensive level plains provision of drainage, a change from traditional to intensive cropping and proper irrigation management are essential. Application of nitrogen and phosphorus is needed to obtain sustained high crop yields. Deficiency of organic matter is also a problem, but intensive cropping with good management helps overcome it to a large extent. The same applies to the problems connected with the high lime content of many Yermosols. Some areas of Calcic Yermosols with 200 to 300 mm rainfall (e.g. in Syria and Iraq) can be used for production of barley or wheat only if the farm is large, so that the farmer can live on one successful crop for three or even four years. Proper soil conservation measures are very necessary, but it would be better to use these areas for grazing. Gypsic and Calcic Yermosols, especially those with petrogypsic and petrocalcic horizons at shallow depth, are generally unsuitable for cropping, with or without irrigation. They can be used only as grazing land. Calcic Yermosols may be used for irrigated wheat, barley and alfalfa where better soils are not available.

Z. Solonchaks

Use. Solonchaks apparently occur in all countries of the region, with the possible exception of Nepal and Bhutan. In humid areas such as Bangladesh, Sri Lanka and southern India, they are associated with tidal flooding in coastal areas. In northern India and elsewhere, they generally occur in alluvial plains affected by saline ground water or by accumulation of salts from collection and evaporation of natural runoff. Orthic and Gleyic Solonchaks occur extensively in all arid and semiarid areas between northern India and the Mediterranean coast. In general, the soils are either bare or support a scanty halophytic vegetation which provides sparse grazing for livestock living mainly off better vegetation on adjoining less saline soils. In some places they are irrigated, generally for poor crops of barley or rice. In Saudi Arabia a local practice is to cover the soils with sand in order to produce irrigated cereal and vegetable crops. The added material soon becomes salinized, however, and if it is not covered with fresh sand a new site must be sought.

Suitability. Solonchaks are fundamentally poor soils, and in many cases they are not worth improving. For development under irrigation, drainage is required to lower the water table and large quantities of water are needed to leach salts from the root zone. Quite often the soil develops an alkalinity problem after leaching, the clay is dispersed and the soil becomes impervious. In such cases, application of gypsum is also needed to control the alkalinity. Such a costly and elaborate development undertaking is generally not feasible in view of the dearth of capital and the low level of know-how of the farmer. However, irrigation development is feasible where the soil contains gypsum and has at least reasonably good permeability, as in Iraq and Iran. The use of tube-wells for deep drainage, as in Pakistan, may be capable of wider application, especially where the aquifer is unconfined and the ground water can be used for irrigation either directly or by mixing it with canal water. Reclamation of Solonchak soils may not be economic in areas where the supply of irrigation water is limited and where there are better soils on which the use of scarce water could provide greater benefits, as in most of the arid and semiarid parts of the region.

Conclusions

Aridity is the main feature of the major part of South Asia, that is, in the area west of India. The main soils are Calcic Yermosols, Lithosols and Calcaric Regosols. Together, these soils account for about 50% of the region's area, most of which is used only for grazing. Cropping is limited to irrigated areas of deep Haplic and Calcic Yermosols. Production from these soils can be improved by extending irrigation, but such possibilities are usually limited. However, production of supplemental fodder for livestock on part of the irrigated area may help to make livestock production secure and profitable.

Luvisols, Nitosols and Acrisols together cover about 25% of the total area of South Asia. They occur in large areas in Burma and Sri Lanka and in about one third of India. Chromic and Ferric Luvisols and Dystric Nitosols are the most extensive soil units, while Eutric Nitosols and Orthic and Humic Acrisols also cover considerable areas. Chromic Luvisols occur in small parts of Lebanon, Israel, Jordan, and Syria. All these soils are generally low in fertility, especially low in available phosphate, and many areas are low in bases as well. Over more than half of the area moisture shortage is an additional limitation.

Vertisols cover about 10% of South Asia. They are very extensive in India, covering about 25% of its area, but also occur in other countries, mainly in semiarid areas. They are quite fertile, and are low only in available phosphate. However, they are difficult to till and have poor internal drainage. Areas of Pellic Vertisols often have poor surface drainage as well. Mechanization of tillage operations, supplemental irrigation and provision of drainage in low-lying areas are needed to increase production from these soils.

Fluvisols, (mainly Eutric and Calcaric Fluvisols) cover about 5% of the subcontinent. They are the most extensive soils in Bangladesh, where most areas are flooded by rivers and land use depends upon the intensity and duration of flooding. Generally they are fertile soils and remain productive despite the low level of manuring. With proper management, two good crops of rice a year can be produced in high rainfall areas. In the Indus plains supplemental irrigation is needed to increase production. In arid areas, as in the Mesopotamian plain, crop production is possible only with irrigation.

Eutric and Dystric Cambisols, occurring in mountainous high rainfall areas of the Himalayas and the Elburz mountains, account for about 5% of the subcontinent's area. As the mountain slopes are usually steep, soil erosion is the main problem. They are best kept under forest; cultivation is possible only with bench terracing. Some areas are, however, very suitable for fruit orchards.

Xerosols, which cover about 5% of the subcontinent, are marginal land for rainfed cropping. Although major improvements depend on irrigation, a significant increase in production can be made by including a drought-resistant legume in crop rotation with wheat and barley. However, the legume must be supplied with phosphate fertilizer.

References

ALTAIE, F.H. *The soils of Iraq.* Ghent, State University of
1968 Ghent. (Thesis) (Mimeographed)

BILENSOY, M.C. Crop productivity as affected by some sys-
1970 tems of rotation in dry-farming areas of Turkey. *Proceedings of the Third FAO/Rockefeller Foundation Wheat Seminar held in Ankara, Turkey, in 1970,* p. 328-330. Rome, FAO.

BURINGH, P. *Soils and soil conditions in Iraq,* p. 67-74. Bagh-
1960 dad, Ministry of Agriculture.

DAN, J. *et al. The soils and soil associations map of Israel.* Jeru-
1962 salem, Ministry of Agriculture and the Hebrew University of Jerusalem.

DEWAN, M.L. & FAMOURI, J. *The soils of Iran.* Rome,
1964 FAO. FAO and Soil Institute of Iran.

FAO. *Characteristics and problems of agriculture in India.*
1956 Rome. Background Country Studies No. 10.

FAO. *Mediterranean Development Project. Iraq country re-
1959 port.* Rome.

FAO. *Mediterranean Development Project. Lebanon country
1959 report.* Rome.

FAO. *Report to the Government of Nepal on soil survey inves-
1965 tigations and soil analysis.* Rome. FAO/EPTA Report No. 2043.

FAO. *Hydro-agricultural development progress. Second interim
1968 report to the Government of Saudi Arabia.* Rome.

FAO. *Soil fertility/fertilizer project in Ceylon. Report to the
1969 Government of Ceylon.* Rome. FAO No. 40, Volume 1.

FAO. *Development of the Sittang river valley. Soils and
1971 land classification for irrigation on the Sinthe Project, Burma.* UNDP/SF Project Burma 13. (Draft Report)

FAO. *Soil resources of East Pakistan.* Rome. FAO/UNDP
1971 Soil Survey Project, Pakistan.

FAO. *Soil resources in West Pakistan and their development
1971 possibilities. Technical Report.* Rome. FAO/UNDP Soil Survey Project, Pakistan.

FAO. *Soil survey and soil and water management research and demonstration in the Rajasthan canal area. Soil survey and land classification. 1.2. Semidetailed soil survey of Anupgarh Shakha area.* Rome.

GIBBS, G.K. *Report to the Government of Iraq on soil conservation.* Rome, FAO.

INDIA. MINISTRY OF FOOD AND AGRICULTURE. *Indian
1958 agricultural Atlas.* New Delhi.

MOORMANN, F.R. *Report to the Government of Jordan on
1959 the soils of east Jordan.* Rome. FAO/EPTA Report No. 1132.

MOORMANN, F.R. & PANABOKKE, C.R. *Soils of Ceylon.* Co
1961 lombo, Government Press. FAO and Land Use Division, Department of Agriculture.

OSMAN, A. *Contribution à l'étude des sols du Liban nord.*
1971 Gand, Université de l'Etat à Gand.

PANABOKKE, C.R. The great soil groups of Ceylon and their
1962 approximate distribution. [*Report of the*] First Seminar on Soil Correlation for South and Central Asia, Tashkent, U.S.S.R., 14 September - 2 October 1962, p. 81-86. Rome, FAO. World Soil Resources Report No. 4.

PEARSON, F.B. Alternative uses of marginal rainfall areas.
1970 *Proceedings of the Third FAO/Rockefeller Foundation Wheat Seminar held in Ankara, Turkey, in 1970,* p. 323-327. Rome, FAO.

RANDHAWA, M.S. *Agriculture and animal husbandry in India.*
1958 New Delhi, Indian Council of Agricultural Research.

RAYCHAUDHURI, S.P. *et al. Soils of India.* New Delhi, Indian
1963 Council of Agricultural Research.

ROZANOV, B.G. *Explanatory note to the soil map of Burma.*
1959 Rangoon, Land Use Bureau. (Mimeographed)

SHAMOOT, S.A. & HUSSINI, K. *Land and water use in the Hashem-*
1969 *ite Kingdom of Jordan. Part I, Land Resources.* A
    paper submitted to the Near East Land and Water Use
    Meeting held in Amman, Jordan in May 1969. Am-
    man, Al Hurieh.

SMITH, R. *Report on the soils of the Yemen highlands.* Rome,
1970 FAO. (Mimeographed)

SUBRAMANIAN, V.S. *et al. Survey of land and water resources,*
1965 *Afghanistan.* Volume 4, *Soils.* Rome, FAO. (FAO/SF
    9 AFG).

TESCO/FAO. *Summary of agricultural potential of Wadi Zabid*
1971 *soils and land capability. Yemen Arab Republic.* Report
    by TESCO, VIZITERV-VITUKI, Budapest, 1971 for FAO,
    Rome.

UNITED NATIONS. *A concise summary of the world popu-*
1971 *lation situation in 1970.* New York. Population studies
    No. 48.

VAN LIERE, W.J. *Report to the Government of Syria on the*
1965 *classification and rational utilization of soils.* Rome,
    FAO. FAO/EPTA Report No. 2075.

Morphological, chemical and physical properties of South Asian soils: data from selected profiles

In this Appendix data are presented on typical profiles representing several of the major soil units that occur as dominant or associated soils on the Soil Map of South Asia.

The profiles were selected from published and unpublished material available to the project. Whenever possible acknowledgement is made to the sources of the data that have been used.

The purpose of including these descriptions and tables is to help define more clearly the nature of the soil units used in the map. Naturally, the description and analyses of one or two profiles will not show the range of characteristics within such broad units but, combined with the definitions in Volume I and with the descriptions and analyses in the other volumes, they should help at least to establish the concepts on which the legend is based.

For most of the soil units only one profile is described. However, for some of the more extensive units two profiles are presented to give some impression of the range that can be expected.

The data have been set out systematically to include most of the items generally available in survey reports. With such a variety of sources there is of course considerable diversity in the information supplied. However, an attempt has been made to present it as uniformly as possible so that valid comparisons can be made. Where established standards such as the U.S. Department of Agriculture *Soil Survey Manual* (Soil Survey Staff, 1951) have been used, there is no difficulty. In other places there may be some uncertainty in the definition of terms, and care in interpretation is needed.

Presentation of data

Whenever possible the data have been taken from the original documents without alteration. However, some changes have been made for the sake of brevity or uniformity of presentation.

SITE DESCRIPTION

The information used to describe the site is as follows:

Location: An attempt was made to locate the site of each profile by the distance and direction from a main town, and by latitude and longitude. In many reports insufficient information was given to determine accurate siting.

Altitude: The altitude is given in metres above mean sea level.

Physiography: Where possible, the nature of the landscape is given.

Drainage: The drainage description is usually given, as in the U.S. Department of Agriculture *Soil Survey Manual*, as a synthesis of runoff, permeability and internal soil drainage.

Parent material: Sometimes parent rock is given under this heading.

Vegetation: Only general terms are used to describe the kind of natural plant cover or present land use.

Climate: The climate is given as an index figure according to the system of Papadakis (1966), outlined in Chapter 4. As a general description, the name of the subgroup is also included.

PROFILE DESCRIPTION

Only minor, if any, changes have been made in the profile descriptions. The pattern outlined in *Guidelines for soil profile description* (FAO) is followed in most cases. Horizon designations have been altered to conform with the definitions given in Volume I. Where they were not included in the original description, they have been added on the basis of the descriptive and analytical information available.

ANALYSES

When considering analyses it is important to know the methods that have been used. In most reports these are described or at least outlined, and a reference is given. Where this is not done, it is often possible to find the information in other publications.

The following publications contain details of most of the methods used:

Bangladesh - *Soil resources of Bangladesh*. FAO, 1971. Technical Report No. 3.

Iran - Soil Institute, FAO/UNDP Project, 1972. Soil and Water Laboratory working papers.

Iraq - *The soils of Iraq*. F.H. Altaie, 1969.

Lebanon - *Soil survey and related irrigation schemes*. FAO, 1969. Final Report, Vol. 4.

Pakistan - *Summary of land capability, West Pakistan*. 1970. FAO/UNDP Soil Survey Project, Pakistan, Project Technical Guide No. 21.

Figures have sometimes been rounded for the sake of uniformity.

pH is usually measured on saturated soil paste, but 1:1 and 1:2.5 soil/water ratios are also used. Measurements in N KCl are given where they are available.

Particle size analysis. Unless otherwise specified, the international system is used to determine the size limits of soil separates.

Cation exchange capacity (CEC). Methods used to determine CEC vary from country to country. In Bangladesh and Pakistan soil is saturated with $BaCl_2$, then shaken with a known amount of $MgSO_4$ and centrifuged. The remaining Mg is determined in an aliquot of the supernatant liquid by titration with EDTA, using eriochrome black T indicator, and substracted from a blank determination for calculation of CEC.

Exchangeable cations. In various countries including Pakistan and Bangladesh, Ca and Mg are determined by titration with EDTA after extraction with ammonium acetate at pH7. They are not determined in calcareous soils. Na and K are determined by flame photometer after extraction with ammonium acetate at pH7. Corrections for soluble Ca, Mg, Na and K are made in samples which contain significant amounts of soluble salts. In Lebanon Ca and Mg are determined by Versemate titration, after extraction with ammonium chloride.

Organic matter. The Walkley-Black method, with or without modification, is used.

Nitrogen. The Kjeldahl method is generally used. In Pakistan and Bangladesh a semi-micro Kjeldahl method using a selenium-copper catalyst is used.

Calcium carbonate. The calcimeter method with HCl is used.

Soluble salts are quoted as electrical conductivity (E.C.) in mmhos/cm at 25°C of a saturated soil paste or saturation extract.

Other analyses are explained in the tables where necessary.

Discussion

Because of the limited number of profiles presented, it is not possible to discuss the properties of the soil units in any detail. Furthermore, profiles were not sampled specifically to characterize the particular soil units, but rather were selected as satisfactory representatives of the various units within the limits of the data available.

The variations may be looked at in two ways. First, there are the variations in properties from unit

LIST OF SOIL PROFILES

Symbol and unit			Country	Page
Bd	CAMBISOL	Dystric	Bangladesh	76
Be		Eutric	Bangladesh	78
Bh		Humic	Bangladesh	80
Bk		Calcic	Lebanon	82
Ge	GLEYSOL	Eutric	Bangladesh	84
Jc	FLUVISOL	Calcaric	Bangladesh	86
Je		Eutric	Bangladesh	88
Lc	LUVISOL	Chromic	India	90
Lc		Chromic	Lebanon	92
Nd	NITOSOL	Dystric	Bangladesh	94
Od	HISTOSOL	Dystric	Bangladesh	96
Qc	ARENOSOL	Cambic	Kuwait	98
Rc	REGOSOL	Calcaric	Kuwait	100
So	SOLONETZ	Orthic	India	102
Vc	VERTISOL	Chromic	India	104
Vp		Pellic	India	106
Xh	XEROSOL	Haplic	Pakistan	108
Yh	YERMOSOL	Haplic	Pakistan	110
Yk		Calcic	Iran	112
Yk		Calcic	Kuwait	114
Yy		Gypsic	Iraq	116

to unit, and second there are the variations within each unit.

Despite the scarcity of samples, it is possible to follow a general development pattern in a sequence such as Fluvisols - Cambisols - Luvisols - Acrisols - Ferralsols. The falling pH, falling bases and phosphorus and increasing clay content are examples of the trends present. Some of the differences, of course, follow from the use of such factors as cation exchange capacity, percent base saturation and percent clay in the definitions, but the overall pattern is consistent with our concepts of these soils. The very low levels of potassium and phosphorus in the more developed soils is a notable feature that will be of particular importance in their agricultural development and use.

Differences within the major divisions and subdivisions may also be considered. The differences within major divisions are of particular interest as illustrations of the application of the criteria developed for the definitions of the units. These criteria are numerous and diverse, including morphological, physical, and chemical properties. The data provide many examples; many more may be found in the analyses of soils from other continents.

Soil profiles, of course, are the result of the operation of a complex array of factors. Changes in any given factor do not necessarily show up in clear differences in properties. However, the site information and the morphological, physical and chemical data do give a useful overall picture of each unit. They also help us to understand how the soils were formed, how they are related, how they may be classified and how they may be used.

References

AKRAM, M. *et al.* *Reconnaissance soil survey of Jhang area.*
1968 Rome, FAO; Lahore, Directorate of Soil Survey. FAO/UNDP Soil Survey Project, Pakistan.

ERGUN, H.N. *Report to the Government of Kuwait on reconnaissance soil survey.* Rome, FAO. (FAO/KU/TF 17).
1969

ESPINOSA, E.J. *Reconnaissance soil survey, Pabna district.*
1966 Rome, FAO; Dacca, Directorate of Soil Survey. FAO/UNDP Soil Survey Project, Pakistan.

ESPINOSA, E.J. *Reconnaissance soil survey, Rajshahi district.*
1968 Vol. 2. Appendix. Rome, FAO; Dacca, Directorate of Soil Survey. FAO/UNDP Soil Survey Project, Pakistan.

FAO. *Guidelines for soil profile description.* Rome, FAO. 53 p.
1968

FAO. [*Report of the*] *Meeting on Soil Correlation and Soil Resources Appraisal in India held in New Delhi, India, 5-15 April 1965.* Rome, FAO.
1965

FAO. *Soil resources of Bangladesh.* Rome. Technical Report No. 3. FAO/UNDP Soil Survey Project, Pakistan.
1971

RAFIQ, M. *Reconnaissance soil survey. Gujrat district.* Rome, FAO; Lahore, Directorate of Soil Survey. FAO/UNDP Soil Survey Project, Pakistan.
1967

SYAL, M.N. *Reconnaissance soil survey of Sargodha. Second edition.* Rome, FAO. Soil Survey Project of Pakistan, Lahore.
1969

U.S. SOIL CONSERVATION SERVICE. *Soil survey manual.* Washington, D.C., U.S. Department of Agriculture. Handbook No. 18. 503 p.
1951

VAN DE WEG, R.F. *et al.* *Semi-detailed soil survey of Sarghaleh area, Ostan Kermanshah, Iran.* Tehran, Ministry of Agriculture, Soil Institute.
1967

VERHEYE, W. *Formation, classification and land evaluation of soils in Mediterranean areas, with special reference to the southern Lebanon.* Ghent, State University of Ghent. (Thesis) (Mimeographed)
1972

DYSTRIC CAMBISOL   **Bd**

Brown hill soil	Bangladesh
FAO, 1971	p. 168-169
Location	Amrail tea estate, Srimangal thana, approx. 24° 40'N, 92°E
Altitude	About 100 m
Physiography	Hilly to mountainous with steep slopes
Drainage	Well drained
Parent material	Tertiary calcareous clays, little consolidated
Vegetation	Tea plantation
Climate	1.9, hot tropical, cool winter, monsoon

Profile description

Ap	0-10	cm	Yellowish brown (10YR 5/4) dry; very fine sandy clay loam; strong coarse and medium granular wormcast structure; hard dry; many fine and common medium tubular pores; common fine roots; pH 4.6; abrupt smooth boundary.
AB	10-32	cm	Yellowish brown (10YR 5/6) dry; very fine sandy clay loam; strong coarse and medium angular blocky; slightly hard dry; many fine and common medium tubular pores; common fine roots; pH 4.6; clear smooth boundary.
Bw1	32-65	cm	Yellowish brown (10YR 5/6) dry; clay loam; strong medium angular blocky; slightly hard dry; many fine and common medium tubular pores; common fine roots; pH 4.7; clear smooth boundary.
Bw2	65-102	cm	Yellowish brown (10YR 5/8) dry; clay loam; strong medium angular blocky; hard dry; many fine and common medium tubular pores; common fine roots; pH 4.7; clear wavy boundary.
Bc	102-130	cm	Brownish yellow (10YR 6/8) moist, with common fine faint strong brown mottles; clay loam; moderate medium angular blocky; hard dry; many fine and common medium tubular pores; common fine roots; pH 5.0; clear smooth boundary.
C1	130-167	cm	Pale olive (5Y 6/3) moist, with common fine faint yellowish brown and few fine distinct dark brown mottles; clay loam; strong medium subangular blocky; hard dry; few fine tubular pores; pH 5.1; clear smooth boundary.
C2	167-182	cm	Greyish brown (2.5Y 5/2) moist, with common medium distinct brownish yellow and yellowish brown mottles; clay loam; strong medium subangular blocky; very hard dry; thin patchy manganese skins along vertical ped faces and pores; pH 5.4.

DYSTRIC CAMBISOL
Bangladesh

Horizon	Depth cm	pH		Cation exchange me %										CaCO₃ %
		H₂O	KCl	CEC	TEB	% BS	Ca	Mg	K	Na	Al	H	
Ap	0—10	4.6		11.5	3.2	28	2.7	0.43	0.03	0.05		8.3	
AB	10—32	4.6											
Bw1	32—65	4.7											
Bw2	65—102	4.7		10.3	3.1	30	[1]3.1		0.01	0.05		7.2	
BC	102—130	5.0											
C1	130—167	5.1											
C2	167—182	5.4											

Horizon	Sol. salts		Organic matter				Particle size analysis %[2]					Flocc. index
	E.C.	ppm	% C	% N	C/N	% OM	Stones	Sand	Silt	Clay	Texture	
Ap			0.83	0.05	17	1.25		55	16	29	Clay loam	
AB			1.52	0.11	14	2.28		53	18	29	Clay loam	
Bw1			1.08	0.08	14	1.62		52	18	30	Clay loam	
Bw2								52	17	31	Clay loam	
BC								52	19	29	Clay loam	
C1			0.71	0.05	14	1.07		50	19	31	Clay loam	
C2	0.6	400						50	19	31	Clay loam	

[1] Ca + Mg.
[2] International size grades unless mentioned otherwise.

EUTRIC CAMBISOL	**Be**

Noncalcareous brown flood-plain soil	Bangladesh
FAO, 1971	p. 164-165
Location	Near Ramchandrapur, Mitapukur thana, 25º 30′N, 89º 30′E
Altitude	About 90 m
Physiography	Gently undulating
Drainage	Moderately well drained
Parent material	Mixed alluvium
Vegetation	Rice in summer and other crops in winter
Climate	1.92, hot tropical; cool winter, monsoon

Profile description

Ap	0-12 cm	Olive brown (2.5Y 4/4) moist to pale olive (5Y 6/3) dry; silt loam; massive, breaking into coarse angular clods; slightly hard dry; friable moist; nonsticky and slightly plastic wet; many fine tubular pores; pH 5.9; abrupt smooth boundary.
B	12-32 cm	Brown (10YR 5/3) moist to pale olive (5Y 6/3) dry; silt loam; weak coarse subangular blocky; slightly hard dry; friable moist nonsticky and slightly plastic wet; many fine tubular and few medium vesicular pores; pH 5.9; clear smooth boundary.
Bc	32-60 cm	Light yellowish brown (2.5Y 6/4) moist; loam; massive; very friable moist; pH 5.9; abrupt wavy boundary.
2C	60-137 cm	Pale olive (5Y 6/3) moist; fine sand; single grain; loose moist; pH 6.2.

EUTRIC CAMBISOL

Bangladesh

Horizon	Depth cm	pH		Cation exchange me %									CaCO₃ %
		H₂O	KCl	CEC	TEB	% BS	Ca	Mg	K	Na	Al	H	
Ap	0—12	5.9		7.3	4.1	57	2.9	0.9	0.20	0.14		3.2	
B	12—32	5.9		7.7	4.1	53	3.4	0.5	0.14	0.08		3.6	
BC	32—60	5.9		3.8	1.4	37	0.8	0.4	0.09	0.08		2.4	
2C	60—137	6.2											

Horizon	Sol. salts	Organic matter				Particle size analysis %					Flocc. index
	E.C.	% C	% N	C/N	% OM	Stones	Sand	Silt	Clay	Texture	
Ap		0.67	0.06	11	1.00		51	35	14	Silt loam	
B		0.49	0.06	8	0.74		45	36	19	Silt loam	
BC		0.18	0.02	9	0.27		52	36	12	Silt loam	
2C	0.05						94	1	5	Sand	

HUMIC CAMBISOL   **Bh**

Black Terai soil	Bangladesh
FAO, 1971	p. 166-167
Location	Lakhipur, Thakargaon thana; 26º 20′N, 89º 10′E
Altitude	About 90 m
Physiography	Nearly level to undulating
Drainage	Imperfectly drained; intermittently flooded by rain water up to a few cm deep in summer
Parent material	Mixed alluvium
Vegetation	Under millet and rice
Climate	1.91, hot tropical; cool winter, monsoon

Profile description

Ap1	**0-10 cm**	Very dark greyish brown (2.5Y 3.5/2) moist to greyish brown (2.5Y 5/2) dry, with common fine faint grey mottles; sandy loam; massive, breaking to weak medium and fine subangular blocky; very friable moist; nonsticky, nonplastic wet; many very fine and fine tubular pores; pH 4.7; abrupt smooth boundary.
Ap2	**10-13 cm**	Very dark greyish brown (10YR 3/2) moist, with common fine distinct dark yellowish brown and grey mottles; sandy loam; massive (plough pan); very friable moist; nonsticky, slightly plastic wet; many very fine and fine tubular pores; pH 5.5; abrupt smooth boundary.
Ah	**13-35 cm**	Very dark greyish brown (10YR 3/2) moist; sandy loam; weak coarse prismatic, breaking to weak medium and fine subangular blocky; very friable moist; nonsticky, nonplastic wet; many very fine and fine tubular pores; pH 5.7; clear wavy boundary.
B	**35-50 cm**	Light olive brown (2.5Y 5/4) moist; sandy loam; weak coarse subangular blocky; very friable moist; nonsticky, nonplastic wet; many very fine and fine tubular pores; pH 6.4; clear smooth boundary.
BC	**50-112 cm**	Light olive brown (2.5Y 5/4) moist; loamy sand; single grain; loose moist; pH 6.5; clear smooth boundary.
C	**112-137 cm**	Grey (5Y 6/1) moist; sand; single grain; loose moist; pH 6.7.

NOTE: Earthworm activity and crotovines are prominent down to about 50 cm.

HUMIC CAMBISOL
Bangladesh

Horizon	Depth cm	pH		Cation exchange me %									CaCO₃ %
		H₂O	KCl	CEC	TEB	% BS	Ca	Mg	K	Na	Al	H	
Ap1	0—10	4.7											
Ap2	10—13	—											
Ah	13—35	5.7											
B	35—50	6.4											
BC	50—112	6.5											
C	112—137	6.7											

Horizon	Sol. salts	Organic matter				Particle size analysis %					Flocc. index
		% C	% N	C/N	% OM	Stones	Sand	Silt	Clay	Texture	
Ap1		1.62	0.16	10	2.43		74	10	16	Sandy loam	
Ap2		—	—	—	—		—	—	—	—	
Ah		1.81	0.13	14	2.72		76	8	16	Sandy loam	
B		0.77	0.07	11	1.16		78	6	16	Sandy loam	
BC		0.14	0.03	5	0.21		90	2	8	Sand	
C		0.17	0.02	8	0.26		96	0	4	Sand	

CALCIC CAMBISOL   **Bk**

Vertic Rendollic Xerochrept   Lebanon

Verheye, 1972   Profile 2, p. 63
Location   15 km south-southwest of Saida 33° 27′N, 35° 18′E
Altitude   160 m
Physiography   Level plateau, dissected near the edges
Drainage   Well drained
Vegetation   Irrigated vegetable crops
Climate   6.1, subtropical moist Mediterranean

Profile description

Ap   0-10   cm   Dark greyish brown (10YR 4/2) moist, and dark brown to brown (10YR 4/3) dry; clay, with 3-15% fine limestone fragments; moderate, fine crumb structure; sticky, plastic, friable; moderately calcareous with local slightly calcareous inclusions; frequent roots and moderate biological activity; clear smooth boundary.

B   10-35   cm   Greyish brown (10YR 4/2) moist, and dark brown (10YR 3.5/3) dry; clay, with 3-15% coarse limestone fragments; strong, medium and fine subangular blocky structure; sticky, plastic, firm, hard; moderately calcareous with some slightly calcareous inclusions; few roots and low porosity; clear smooth boundary.

C   35-55   cm   Yellowish brown (10YR 5/4) moist, and brown (10YR 5/3) dry; silty clay, with 15-25% fine and coarse limestone fragments; massive, with a tendency to a fine, subangular blocky structure; nonsticky, slightly plastic, friable, hard; moderately calcareous; abrupt broken boundary.

R   55+   cm   Soft marly limestone.

CALCIC CAMBISOL

Lebanon

Horizon	Depth cm	pH		Cation exchange me %										CaCO₃ %
		H₂O	KCl	CEC	TEB	% BS	Ca	Mg	K	Na	Al	H	
Ap	0—10	8.6		32.6	30.3		25.6	4.0	0.15	0.50			36.5
B	10—35	8.6		31.4	30.0		26.4	2.4	0.42	0.77			38.0
C	35—55	8.7		26.0	26.5		23.6	2.0	0.42	0.52			52.0
R	55+	—											84.5

Horizon	Sol. salts	Organic matter				Particle size analysis %					Flocc. index	Free Fe₂O₃
		% C	% N	C/N	% OM	Stones	Sand	Silt U.S.	Clay	Texture		
Ap		0.77	0.09	8.2			9.2	39.3	51.5	Clay		2.01
B		0.87	0.09	9.4			11.3	39.5	49.2	Clay		1.90
C		0.46	0.07	7.0			14.5	42.5	43.0	Silty clay		1.26
R		—	—	—								0.68

EUTRIC GLEYSOL   Ge

Typic Haplaquept	Bangladesh
Espinosa, 1968	Digli series, p. 25 and 115
Location	Naogaon, Rajshali district, 24° 30'N, 88° 45'E
Altitude	About 100 m
Physiography	Nearly level broad basin
Drainage	Poorly drained; flooded about 2 m deep for 4 to 5 months; unsaturated for about 5 months in winter
Parent material	Clayey alluvium
Vegetation	Under rice
Climate	1.91, hot tropical; cool winter, monsoon

Profile description

Apg1   0-8   cm   Dark grey (5Y 4/1) moist to grey (5Y 5/1) dry with common fine prominent strong brown mottles; clay; massive breaking into coarse angular clods; very hard dry, firm moist, sticky, plastic wet; common fine tubular pores; abrupt smooth boundary; pH 4.6.

Apg2   8-13   cm   Dark grey (5Y 4/1) moist with many medium prominent strong brown mottles; clay; massive; very firm moist, sticky, plastic wet; few fine tubular pores; abrupt smooth boundary; pH 5.5.

Bwg1   13-48   cm   Grey (5Y 5/1) moist with many fine and medium prominent yellowish brown and light olive brown mottles; clay; strong very coarse prismatic breaking into strong coarse and medium angular blocky; very firm moist, sticky, plastic wet; continuous thick dark grey cutans along vertical and horizontal ped faces; common very fine and fine tubular pores; clear smooth boundary; pH 5.6.

Bwg2   48-73   cm   Grey (5Y 5/1) moist with many fine and medium prominent yellowish brown mottles; clay; moderate coarse prismatic firm moist, sticky, plastic wet, continuous moderately thick dark grey cutans along vertical ped faces; common very fine and fine tubular pores; clear smooth boundary; pH 6.0.

BCg   73-100   cm   Very dark greyish brown (2.5Y 3/2) moist with common fine distinct dark yellowish brown mottles; clay loam; weak coarse angular blocky; firm moist, slightly sticky, slightly plastic wet; patchy thin grey cutans along vertical ped faces; very few, small, soft, spherical iron-manganese nodules; common very fine and fine tubular pores; abrupt smooth boundary; pH 5.9.

2Cg   100-138   cm   Grey (5Y 5/1) and yellowish brown (10YR 5/6) moist; clay loam; structure not recorded; slightly sticky, slightly plastic wet; very few, small, soft and hard, spherical iron-manganese nodules; pH 6.0.

EUTRIC GLEYSOL

Bangladesh

Horizon	Depth cm	pH		Cation exchange me %										CaCO₃ %
		H₂O	KCl	CEC	TEB	% BS	Ca	Mg	K	Na	Al	H	
Apg1	0—8	4.6		19.0	10.8	57	7.3	2.7	0.52	0.32		8.2	
Bwg1	13—48	5.6		25.8	20.1	78	14.6	4.9	0.33	0.28		5.7	
Bwg2	48—73	6.0		20.4	15.8	77	11.0	4.2	0.24	0.34		4.6	
BCg	73—100	5.9		14.7	11.0	75	6.6	4.0	0.19	0.24		3.7	
2Cg	100—138	6.0					—	—	—	—		—	

Horizon	Sol. salts	Organic matter				Particle size analysis %					Flocc. index
		% C	% N	C/N	% OM	Stones	Sand	Silt	Clay	Texture	
Apg1		2.43	0.19	13			20	24	56	Clay/silty clay	
Bwg1		1.18	0.15	8			5	17	78	Clay	
Bwg2		0.74	0.08	9			18	22	60	Clay	
BCg		—					47	18	35	Clay loam	
2Cg		—					45	18	37	Clay/clay loam	

CALCARIC FLUVISOL   Jc

Calcareous alluvium   Bangladesh

FAO, 1971   p 148-149
Location   Horni, Hatiya thana, approx. 23°N, 91°E
Altitude   About 30 m
Physiography   Nearly level
Drainage   Seasonally poorly drained; flooded up to 0.3-0.6 m for 3 to 4 months.
Parent material   Calcareous, mixed alluvium
Vegetation   Under rice and winter pulses
Climate   1.92, hot tropical; cool winter, monsoon

Profile description

Apg1   0-12 cm   Olive (5Y 4/3) moist, with yellowish brown (10YR 5/8) dark yellowish brown (10YR 4/4) and greenish grey mottles; silt loam; structureless (massive); friable moist; common fine roots; common fine tubular pores; pH 6.8; clear smooth boundary.

Apg2   12-17 cm   Olive grey (5Y 5/2) moist, with common coarse prominent yellowish red iron staining; silt loam; structureless (massive); friable moist; common fine roots; common fine tubular pores; pH 7.8; slight effervescence with dilute acid; abrupt smooth boundary.

Cg1   17-45 cm   Olive (5Y 5/3) moist, with common fine faint light grey (5Y 7/1) mottles; silt loam; finely stratified, with thin patchy grey coatings along vertical cracks; friable moist; few fine tubular pores; pH 8.3; strong effervescence with dilute acid; clear smooth boundary.

Cg2   45-75 cm   Olive (5Y 4/3) moist, with common fine faint light grey (5Y 7/1) and light olive brown mottles; silt loam; finely stratified; friable moist; thin nearly continuous grey coatings on vertical cracks; few medium tubular pores; pH 8.3; strong effervescence with dilute acid; gradual smooth boundary.

Cg3   75-105 cm   Olive (5Y 5/4) moist, with few fine faint grey (5Y 5/1) mottles; silt loam; finely stratified; very friable moist; pH 8.3; slight effervescence with dilute acid; gradual smooth boundary.

2Cg   105-135 cm   Olive (5Y 5/4) moist, with common medium distinct dark yellowish brown (10YR 4/4) and few fine faint light grey mottles; silty clay loam; stratified; friable moist; pH 8.3; slight effervescence with dilute acid; diffuse smooth boundary.

3Cg   135-162 cm   Olive (5Y 4/4) moist, with common medium distinct dark yellowish brown (10YR 3/4) mottles; silt loam; very friable moist; pH 8.4; slight effervescence with dilute acid.

CALCARIC FLUVISOL

Bangladesh

Horizon	Depth cm	pH		Cation exchange me%										CaCO₃ %
		H₂O	KCl	CEC	TEB	% BS	Ca	Mg	K	Na	Al	H	
Apg1	0—12			11.43	9.81	86	7.44	1.52	0.12	0.73		1.62	
Apg2	12—17												
Cg1	17—45			8.88					0.10	0.50			
Cg2	45—75												
Cg3	75—105												
2Cg	105—135			14.26					0.24	0.73			
3Cg	135—162												

Horizon	Sol. salts	Organic matter				Particle size analysis %					Flocc. index
		% C	% N	C/N	% OM	Stones	Sand	Silt	Clay	Texture	
Apg1		0.97	0.07	14	1.46		22.8	54.2	23.0	Silt	
Apg2		0.57	0.04	14	0.86		18.9	55.1	26.0	Silt/silty clay loam	
Cg1		0.24	0.02	12	0.36		25.9	59.5	14.6	Silt	
Cg2		—					28.1	55.1	16.8	Silt	
Cg3		—					19.9	59.2	20.9	Silt	
2Cg		—					12.4	58.5	29.1	Silty clay loam	
3Cg		—					30.9	53.3	15.8	Silt	

EUTRIC FLUVISOL	**Je**
Noncalcareous alluvium	Bangladesh
FAO, 1971	p. 146-147
Location	Gopalpur thana, Tangail subdivision, approx. 24º 30'N, 90ºE
Altitude	About 50 m
Physiography	Gently undulating
Drainage	Seasonally poorly drained; flooded up to 0.7 m for about 10 days in summer
Parent material	Noncalcareous, mixed alluvium
Vegetation	Under rice
Climate	1.92, hot tropical; cool winter, monsoon

Profile description

Ap **0-12 cm** Grey (5Y 5/1) moist, with few fine distinct yellowish brown mottles; silt loam; moderate fine cloddy, with remnants of stratification; friable moist, slightly plastic and slightly sticky wet; few fine tubular pores; many fine roots; pH 7.3; clear smooth boundary.

Cg1 **12-20 cm** Grey (N 6) and dark greyish brown (2.5Y 4/2) moist, with common fine distinct brown (7.5YR 4/4) mottles; silt loam; massive; finely stratified; very friable moist; common fine tubular pores; common fine roots; pH 7.5; abrupt smooth boundary.

Cg2 **20-55 cm** Olive grey (5Y 4/2) wet, with common fine faint olive brown mottles; silt loam; massive; very finely stratified; friable moist; plastic and slightly sticky wet; thin, nearly continuous ferric iron coatings on vertical cracks about 15 cm apart; few fine tubular pores; few fine roots concentrated along vertical cracks; pH 7.4; abrupt smooth boundary.

Cg3 **55-73 cm** Colour not recorded; silt loam; stratified; pH 7.3; abrupt smooth boundary.

2C **73-87 cm** Colour not recorded; silty clay loam; abrupt smooth boundary.

3C **87-120 cm** Fine sand.

EUTRIC FLUVISOL

Bangladesh

Horizon	Depth cm	pH		Cation exchange me %									CaCO₃ %
		H₂O	KCl	CEC	TEB	% BS	Ca	Mg	K	Na	Al	H	
Ap	0—12			13.4									
Cg1	12—20			10.1								0.7	
Cg2	20—55			13.09	11.89	91	10.2	1.4	0.16	0.13		1.2	
Cg3	55—73			11.63	10.43	90	8.8	1.5	0.06	0.07		1.2	

Horizon	Sol. salts	Organic matter				Particle size analysis %					Flocc. index
	E.C.	% C	% N	C/N	% OM	Stones	Sand	Silt	Clay	Texture	
Ap		0.57	0.04	14	0.86		35	47	18	Silt loam	
Cg1		0.31	0.02	16	0.46		60	32	8	Silt loam	
Cg2		0.61	0.04	15	0.92		27	55	18	Silt	
Cg3	0.22						26	20	4	Loamy sand	

CHROMIC LUVISOL   Lc

Deep red loam	India
FAO, 1965	p. 86-87
Location	Bangalore-Tumkur road near Km 14. Approx. 13ºN 77ºE
Altitude	About 700 m
Physiography	Gently undulating
Drainage	Well drained
Parent material	Gneiss
Vegetation	Short grass, a few thorny shrubs and some trees
Climate	1.4, hot tropical

Profile desrciption

Ah   0-13   cm   Yellowish red (5YR 4/6) dry, reddish brown (5YR 4/3-4/4) moist; sandy loam with very fine shiny sand grains; fine root channels and number of small pores; moderate medium crumb structure; soft when dry, friable when moist and slightly sticky when wet; abundant grass roots; clear smooth boundary.

BA   13-56   cm   Red (2.5YR 4/6) dry, dark red (2.5YR 3/6) moist; loam with scattered fine quartz gravel; moderate medium subangular blocky structure; slightly hard when dry, friable when moist and slightly sticky and plastic when wet; abundant fine and few big roots; diffuse boundary.

Bt1   56-92   cm   Dark red (2.5YR 3/6) dry and moist; clay loam; moderate medium subangular blocky breaking to fine subangular blocky structure; slightly hard when dry, friable when moist, sticky and plastic when wet; diffuse boundary.

Bt2   92-150 cm   Yellowish red (6YR 4/6) dry, reddish brown (5YR 4/4) moist; clay loam to clay with scattered fine quartz gravel; moderate crumb to weak blocky; number of pores; hard when dry, slightly firm when moist and sticky when wet; diffuse boundary.

BC   150-183 cm   Yellowish red (5YR 4/8) dry, yellowish red (5YR 4/6) moist; gravelly clay loam with 30-40% quartz gravel of 0.5-20 mm size and few ferruginous and manganese concretions; moderate medium subangular blocky structure; hard when dry and sticky when wet.

C   183   cm   Weathered gneiss

CHROMIC LUVISOL

India

Horizon	Depth cm	pH		Cation exchange me %										CaCO₃ %
		H₂O	KCl	CEC	TEB	% BS	Ca	Mg	K	Na	Al	H	
Ah	0—13	6.7		6.5			0.100						
BA	13—56	6.5		9.1			0.100						
Bt1	56—92	6.5		8.5			0.105						
Bt2	92—150	6.6		9.6			0.120						
BC	150—183	6.6		11.3			0.135						

Horizon	Sol. salts	Organic matter				Particle size analysis %						Flocc. index
	E.C.	% C	% N	C/N	% OM	Stones	Coarse sand	Fine sand	Silt	Clay	Texture	
Ah	0.30	0.87					33.95	35.60	13.92	14.68	Loam	
BA	<0.1	0.60					33.25	22.75	10.52	31.08	Clay loam	
Bt1	<0.1	0.45					28.25	23.00	14.60	32.60	Clay loam	
Bt2	<0.1	0.33					27.45	27.25	11.76	32.24	Clay loam	
BC	<0.1	0.30					29.20	20.55	13.60	33.40	Clay loam	

Horizon	Water-holding capacity	Moisture equivalent	Total CaO %	Total P₂O₅ %	Total K₂O %
Ah	34.94	13.86	0.196	0.0033	0.224
BA	41.16	16.09	0.140	0.0036	0.469
Bt1	40.33	19.16	0.140	0.0012	0.432
Bt2	38.69	18.04	0.182	0.0093	0.116
BC	32.58	20.52	0.210	0.0047	0.249

CHROMIC LUVISOL Lc

Rendollic Haploxeraf Lebanon

Verheye, 1972 Profile 5, p. 91

Location 300 m west of Sfarai, 33° 33′N, 35° 29′E

Altitude 450 m

Physiography Slightly sloping plateau with steeply dissected edges, in karst landscape

Drainage Somewhat imperfectly drained

Parent material Hard dolomitic limestone, permeable

Vegetation Mediterranean evergreen oak forest

Climate 6.1, subtropical moist Mediterranean

Profile description

Ah **0-14 cm** Dark reddish brown (5YR 3/4) moist and dry; clay, with 3-15% limestone gravel; strong, medium and coarse granular structure; very sticky, very plastic, firm, very hard; noncalcareous; frequent roots; medium porosity and biological activity. Clear smooth boundary.

Bt **14-39 cm** Dark reddish brown (5YR 3/4) moist and dry; clay, with 3-15% limestone gravel; strong, medium and fine angular blocky structure, often regrouped into coarse, subangular elements; very sticky, very plastic, firm, very hard; continuous fine cutans on the fine peds; noncalcareous; common roots, low porosity and biological activity. Clear gradual boundary.

BC **39-80 cm** Yellowish brown (5YR 4/6) moist and dry, with a strong brown (7.5YR 5/6) diffuse mottling; clay, with 3-15% limestone fragments; moderate, medium and fine angular blocky structure, often regrouped to coarse and medium subangular elements; very sticky, very plastic, firm, very hard; discontinuous fine cutans on the fine peds; almost noncalcareous; no roots; very low porosity and biological activity. Inclusions of some diffuse, strong brown (7.5YR 5/6) calcareous, clayey soil material, without apparent structure, are observed immediately underneath coarse limestone fragments in the horizon. Abrupt interrupted boundary.

R **80+ cm** Hard dolomitic limestone, disintegrating into numerous fragments of different sizes and shapes.

CHROMIC LUVISOL
Lebanon

Horizon	Depth cm	pH		Cation exchange me %									CaCO₃ %
		H₂O	KCl	CEC	TEB	% BS	Ca	Mg	K	Na	Al	H	
Ah	0—14	8.1	6.6	26.6	23.7		18.8	3.6	0.63	0.70			0
Bt	14—39	8.0	6.4	27.0	24.0		18.8	4.0	0.46	0.70			4.5
BC	39—80	8.4	7.2	25.0	22.1		18.8	2.8	0.21	0.27			16.5
BC1	39—80	8.4	7.0	—			—		—	—			24.5

Horizon	Sol. salts	Organic matter				Particle size analysis %					Flocc. index	Free Fe₂O₃
		% C	% N	C/N	% OM	Stones	Sand	Silt	Clay	Texture		
Ah		2.56	0.31	8.2			9.5	19.1	71.4	Clay		9.07
Bt		1.04	0.21	5.0			7.9	15.6	76.5	Clay		9.26
BC		0.56	0.15	3.7			11.9	15.3	72.8	Clay		8.00
BC1		0.72	—	—			16.8	11.1	72.1	Clay		7.30

[1] Calcareous material beneath coarse lime fragments.

DYSTRIC NITOSOL   Nd

Deep red-brown terrace soil   Bangladesh

FAO, 1971	p. 172-173
Location	Nayanpur, Joydepur thana, approx. 24ºN, 90º 15′E
Altitude	About 60 m
Physiography	Nearly level summit of gently rolling, dissected terrace
Drainage	Well to moderately well drained
Parent material	Pleistocene/Tertiary clay
Vegetation	*Shorea robusta* forest
Climate	1.92, hot tropical; cool winter, monsoon.

Profile description

Ah1   **0-4**   **cm**   Dark brown (7.5YR 3/4) moist, brown (7.5YR 5/4) dry; loam; weak fine platy; soft dry; very friable moist; nonsticky, nonplastic wet; many very fine tubular pores; pH 6.1; abrupt smooth boundary.

Ah2   **4-7**   **cm**   Dark brown (7.5YR 4/2) moist, brown (7.5YR 5/4) dry; clay loam; weak fine to medium subangular blocky; slightly hard dry; friable moist; slightly sticky and slightly plastic wet; many very fine tubular pores; pH 5.2; abrupt wavy boundary.

BA   **7-15**   **cm**   Yellowish red (5YR 4/6) moist, reddish yellow (5YR 6/6) dry; clay; weak medium to coarse subangular blocky; hard dry; friable moist; sticky and plastic wet; many very fine tubular pores; pH 5.2; abrupt wavy boundary.

Bt1   **15-47**   **cm**   Red (2.5YR 4/6) moist, light red (2.5YR 6/6) dry; clay; moderate fine subangular blocky; hard dry; firm moist; sticky and plastic wet; many very fine tubular pores; pH 5.2-5.5; gradual smooth boundary.

Bt2   **47-115 cm**   As Bt1; pH 5.6-5.7; gradual smooth boundary.

C1   **115-155 cm**   Red (2.5YR 4/6) moist, light red (2.5YR 6/6) dry, with common fine distinct very pale brown (10YR 7/4) and few fine and medium prominent black (10YR 2/1 dry) mottles; clay; strong fine angular and subangular blocky; hard dry; firm moist; very sticky and very plastic wet; common very fine tubular pores; pH 5.5; gradual smooth boundary.

C2   **155-190 cm**   Reddish brown (2.5YR 4/4 moist, 5/4 dry), with many coarse distinct pale yellow (2.5Y 7/4) and black (10YR 2/1 dry) mottles; clay; strong fine and medium angular and subangular blocky; hard dry; firm moist; very sticky and very plastic wet; common very fine tubular pores; few fine manganese concretions; pH 5.5-5.4.

DYSTRIC NITOSOL

Bangladesh

Horizon	Depth cm	pH		Cation exchange me %										CaCO$_3$ %
		H$_2$O	KCl	CEC	TEB	% BS	Ca	Mg	K	Na	Al	H	
Ah1	0—4	6.1		10.32	5.83	56	3.26	2.02	0.50	0.05		4.49	
Ah2	4—7	5.2											
BA	7—15	5.2		10.84	4.11	38	2.10	1.40	0.50	0.11		6.73	
Bt1	15—31	5.2											
Bt1	31—47	5.5											
Bt2	47—70	5.6											
Bt2	70—95	5.7		9.75	1.54	16	1.02	0.34	0.15	0.03		8.21	
C1	135—155	5.5		11.37	1.96	17	1.02	0.85	0.06	0.03		9.41	

Horizon	Sol. salts E.C.	Organic matter				Particle size analysis %					Flocc. index
		% C	% N	C/N	% OM	Stones	Sand	Silt	Clay	Texture	
Ah1		1.41	0.11	13	2.12		60.1	22.5	17.4	Loam	
Ah2		1.10	0.09	12	1.66		48.2	20.7	31.1	Clay loam	
BA		0.88	0.08	10	1.32		37.7	20.8	41.5	Clay	
Bt1		0.68	0.07	10	1.02		31.9	19.1	49.0	Clay	
Bt1							29.0	18.0	53.0	Clay	
Bt2							27.8	18.0	54.2	Clay	
B2							26.7	18.8	54.5	Clay	
C1	0.07						28.3	18.2	53.5	Clay	

DYSTRIC HISTOSOL   Od

Peat	Bangladesh
FAO, 1971	p. 151
Location	Satla, Banaripara thana; approx. 23°N, 90°E
Altitude	About 5 m
Physiography	Nearly level basin
Drainage	Very poorly drained; seasonally flooded up to 2 m deep
Parent material	Peat and muck
Vegetation	Grasses and reeds; water hyacinth in patches
Climate	1.92, hot tropical; cool winter, monsoon.

Profile description

Ha1   0-20   cm   Sapric horizon: fibres comprise less than 1/3 of the total mass; very dark brown (10YR 2/2) wet; no colour change when pressed firmly; when squeezed in the hand, liquid removed is turbid and over 2/3 of the mass passes between fingers; nonsticky and slightly plastic; abrupt smooth boundary.

Ha2   20-62   cm   Sapric horizon: fibres comprise about 1/3 of total mass; black (5YR 2/1) wet; colour changes to black (10YR 2/1) when pressed firmly; when squeezed in the hand, liquid removed is turbid and nearly 2/3 of the mass passes between fingers.

He1   62-77   cm   Hemic horizon: fibres comprise about 1/2 of total mass; black (5YR 2/1) wet; no colour change when pressed firmly; when squeezed in the hand, liquid removed is turbid and about 1/2 of the total mass oozes between fingers.

He2   77-117   cm   Hemic horizon: fibres comprise about 1/2 of total mass; black (5YR 2/1) wet; colour changes to black (10YR 2/1) when pressed firmly; when squeezed in the hand, liquid removed is turbid and about 1/2 of the total mass oozes between fingers.

Hi   117-150   cm   Fibric horizon: fibres comprise over 2/3 of the total mass; very dark brown (10YR 2/2) wet; colour changes to black (5YR 2/1) when pressed firmly; when squeezed in the hand, liquid removed is clear and less than 1/3 of the total mass oozes between fingers.

DYSTRIC HISTOSOL

Bangladesh

Horizon	Depth cm	pH		Cation exchange me %									CaCO₃ %
		H₂O	KCl	CEC	TEB	% BS	Ca	Mg	K	Na	Al	H	
Ha1	0—20	5.3											
Ha2	20—62	5.5											
He1	62—77	5.7											
He2	77—117	5.4											
Hi	117—150	5.5											

Horizon	Sol. salts	Organic matter				Particle size analysis %					Flocc. index
		% C	% N	C/N	% OM	Stones	Sand	Silt	Clay	Texture	
Ha1		20.39	1.21	17	30.66						
Ha2		35.92	2.24	16	54.00						
He1		50.35	2.51	20	75.72						
He2		48.76	2.38	20	73.32						
Hi		45.09	1.89	24	67.80						

CAMBIC ARENOSOL   **Qc**

Desert soil	Kuwait
Ergun, 1969	Profile 2, p. 49
Location	East of nursery near Kuwait city, approx. 90°N, 48°E
Altitude	About 30 m
Physiography	Level to undulating
Drainage	Moderately well drained
Parent material	Semiconsolidated, calcareous marine sandstone
Vegetation	Mediterranean sparse semidesert shrub; under grazing
Climate	3.2, hot subtropical desert

Profile description

A	0-18 cm	Pale brown (10YR 6/3) to brown (10YR 5/3) moist; loamy sand; weak coarse blocky breaking to single grain; loose; strongly calcareous; small, whitish gravel layer on the surface.
Cck1	18-50 cm	Light yellowish brown to very pale brown (10YR 6.5/4) to yellowish brown to light yellowish brown (10YR 5.5/4) moist; loamy sand; single grain; loose; strongly calcareous; contains some whitish small gravel.
Cck2	50-100 cm	Very pale brown (10YR 8/3) to very pale brown (10YR 7/3) moist; gravelly sandy to loamy sand; slightly hard pan layer; friable; firm; moderately to strongly calcareous.
C	100-148 cm	White (10YR 8/2) to light grey (10YR 7/2) moist; sand; firm; moderately calcareous.

CAMBIC ARENOSOL
Kuwait

Horizon	Depth cm	pH		Cation exchange me %									CaCO₃ %
		H₂O paste	KCl	CEC	TEB	% BS	Ca	Mg	K	Na	Al	H	
A	0—18	8.2		3.32									3.32
Cck1	18—50	8.3		11.73									11.73
Cck2	50—100	8.1		12.45									12.45
C	100—148	8.1		8.24									8.24

Horizon	Sol. salts	Organic matter				Particle size analysis %					Flocc. index
	E.C.	% C	% N	C/N	% OM	Stones/ gravel	Sand	Silt	Clay	Texture	
A	0.80					7.78	82.32	10.30	7.38	Loamy sand	
Cck1	1.40					2.93	88.36	5.15	6.49	Loamy sand	
Cck2	3.20					3.67	88.79	2.60	8.61	Loamy sand	
C	1.40					0.36	90.74	1.67	7.59	Sand	

8

CALCARIC REGOSOL   Rc

Desert soil to Regosol intergrade   Kuwait

Ergun, 1969	Profile No. 5, p. 60
Location	Northwest of Mutla, approx. 29°N, 48°E
Altitude	About 90 m
Physiography	Undulating
Drainage	Excessive
Parent material	Sand
Vegetation	Mediterranean semidesert shrubs
Climate	3.2, hot subtropicaldesert

Profile description

A	0-4 cm	Pale brown (10YR 6/3) to brown (10YR 5/3) moist; loamy sand; weak platy; loose; strongly calcareous; a thin whitish gravel layer on the surface.
Ck1	4-70 cm	Pale brown (10YR 6/3) to brown (10YR 5/3) moist; sand; single grain; loose; more calcareous than the horizon above.
Ck2	70-95 cm	Pale brown to very pale brown (10YR 6.5/3) to yellowish brown (10YR 5/4) moist; sand; single grain; loose; strongly calcareous.
C	95-150 cm	Light grey to very pale brown (10YR 7/2.5) to light grey (10YR 7/2) moist; sand; single grain; loose; moderately calcareous.

CALCARIC REGOSOL

Kuwait

Horizon	Depth cm	pH		Cation exchange me %										CaCO₃ %
		H₂O	KCl	CEC	TEB	% BS	Ca	Mg	K	Na	Al	H		
A	0—4	8.2		6.3										10.31
Ck1	4—30	8.4		4.90										12.65
Ck1	30—70	8.1		5.40										11.07
Ck2	70—95	8.3		6.80										11.28
C	95—130	8.3		8.10										0.95
C	130—150	8.4		8.70										0.92

Horizon	Sol. salts E.C.	Organic matter				Particle size analyiss %					Flocc. index
		% C	% N	C/N	% OM	Stones	Sand	Silt	Clay	Texture	
A	0.45					16.42	83.97	9.58	6.45	Loamy sand	
Ck1	0.38					16.81	85.70	7.93	6.37	Loamy sand	
Ck1	1.20					6.92	88.40	5.91	5.69	Loamy sand	
Ck2	0.20					9.45	89.73	4.42	5.85	Sand	
C	0.28					11.51	92.66	2.37	4.97	Sand	
C	0.35					8.09	95.97	0.22	3.81	Sand	

ORTHIC SOLONETZ   **So**

Saline and alkali soil	India
FAO, 1965	p. 65-67
Location	Near Meerut, Uttar Pradesh state, India, approx. 29°N, 77° 33'E
Altitude	About 250 m
Physiography	Nearly level
Drainage	Imperfectly drained; water table at 2.5 m in March
Parent material	Calcareous, mixed alluvium
Vegetation	Salt and alkali-tolerant grass
Climate	4.2, monsoon subtropical

Profile description

Ah   **0-5 cm**   Light yellowish brown (2.5Y 6/4) dry, light olive brown (2.5Y 5/4) moist; loam; weak fine platy structure; loose to soft; slight effervescence with dilute acid; pH 10.3; plentiful fine roots; clear smooth boundary.

Btn1   **5-30 cm**   Pale yellow (2.5Y 7/4) dry, light yellowish brown (2.5Y 6/4) moist; clay loam; weak subangular blocky and weak prismatic to columnar structure; slightly hard when dry, friable when moist; slight effervescence with dilute hydrochloric acid; pH 10.4; plentiful roots; gradual boundary.

Btn2   **30-60 cm**   Light yellowish brown (2.5Y 6/4) dry, light olive brown (2.5Y 5/4) moist, faint yellowish brown mottles; clay; weak medium blocky; hard when dry and friable when moist; slight effervescence with dilute acid; pH 10.3; few roots; few iron concretions; diffuse boundary.

Btn3   **60-75 cm**   Light yellowish brown (2.5Y 6/4) dry, light olive brown (2.5Y 5/4) moist, distinct yellowish brown mottles; clay; moderate medium blocky; hard when dry, slightly firm when moist; slight effervescence with dilute acid; pH 10.2; few roots; iron concretions more common; gradual boundary.

Btn4   **75-132 cm**   Pale yellow (2.5Y 7/4) dry, light yellowish brown (2.5Y 6/4) moist, distinct yellowish brown mottles; clay; moderate medium blocky structure; hard when dry and slightly firm when moist; slight effervescence with dilute hydrochloric acid; pH 10.0; blackish brown rounded iron concretions increasing in size and number with depth; gradual boundary.

BC   **132-160 cm**   Olive yellow (2.5Y 6/6) dry, light olive brown (2.5Y 5/4) moist; clay loam; weak medium subangular blocky; very hard when dry, firm when moist; slight effervescence with acid; very few iron concretions; gradual boundary.

C   **160+ cm**   Pale yellow (2.5Y 7/4) dry, light yellowish brown (2.5Y 6/4) moist; clay loam; weak subangular blocky; slightly hard when dry; violent effervescence with acid; lime concretions of medium size.

ORTHIC SOLONETZ
India

Horizon	Depth cm	pH H₂O 1:2.5	KCl	CEC	TEB	% BS	Ca	Mg	K	Na	Al	H	CaCO₃ %
							Cation exchange me %						
Ah	0—5	10.3											2.87
Btn1	5—30	10.4											1.51
Btn2	30—60	10.3											0.96
Btn3	60—75	10.2											tr.
Btn4	75—132	10.0											0.16
BC	132—160	9.9											0.24
C	160+	9.7											5.25

Horizon	Sol. salts E.C.	% C	% N	C/N	% OM	Stones	Coarse sand	Fine sand	Silt	Clay	Texture	Flocc. index
		Organic matter				Particle size analysis %						
Ah	30.0	0.23					0.43	54.0	20.7	24.8	Loam/clay loam	
Btn1	9.5	0.07					2.42	38.0	20.7	38.8	Clay	
Btn2	6.0	0.08					1.56	36.8	20.6	41.0	Clay	
Btn3	3.2	0.09					0.81	30.6	19.5	49.1	Clay	
Btn4	1.1	0.06					1.83	34.6	18.8	44.7	Clay	
BC	0.8	0.05					0.93	45.5	17.9	35.6	Clay/clay loam	
C	1.0	0.06					2.43	56.0	12.8	28.6	Clay loam	

Horizon	Na	Ca	Mg	CO₃	HCO₃	SO₄	Cl	Water saturation %	Bulk density
	Soluble cations and anions in saturation extract me/l								
Ah	262.0	8.0	—	125.0	62.0	102.0	14.0	34.8	—
Btn1	91.0	6.0	1.0	50.0	10.0	25.0	7.0	38.4	1.59
Btn2	52.0	6.0	2.0	25.0	20.0	13.1	2.8	36.0	1.76
Btn3	25.0	6.0	1.5	10.0	20.0	3.2	2.8	37.2	1.86
Btn4	7.0	6.0	0.5	5.0	10.0		3.5	51.2	1.90
BC	3.0	6.5	1.0		10.0		4.9	42.4	1.56
C	2.5	6.0	2.0		10.0		4.2	36.4	1.57

CHROMIC VERTISOL   Vc

Very deep black soil	India
FAO, 1965	p. 77-79
Location	7 km south of Isapur, Warda district, Maharashtra state, approx. 21ºN, 78º 30′E
Altitude	About 240 m
Physiography	Level plain in undulating plateau
Drainage	Somewhat poorly drained
Parent material	Basalt
Vegetation	Thorny leguminous and some dry deciduous trees; mainly under sorghum, cotton and wheat
Climate	4.3, hot semitropical, subhumid

Profile description

Ap   0-5   cm   Dark greyish brown (10YR 4/2) crust and mulch, very dark greyish brown (10YR 3/2) with dark grey (2.5YR 3/0) shading when wet; clay; medium granular to buckshot structure; mustard size irregular calcium carbonate concretions spread sparsely, strong effervescence with HCl; loose when dry, friable when moist and sticky when wet; permeability moderately rapid; roots few; clear and smooth boundary.

Ah   5-35   cm   Very dark grey (10YR 3/1) with dark brown (10YR 3/3) shading; clay; coarse columnar; hard when dry, firm when moist and sticky when wet; effervescence with HCl; many fibrous roots; permeability moderate; diffused boundary.

ACh1   35-60 em   Very dark greyish brown (10YR 3/2) with very dark grey (10YR 3/1) shading; clay; strong subangular blocky with little gravel; few lime nodules giving slight effervescence with HCl; very hard when dry, very firm when moist and very sticky when wet; many fine fibrous roots along cracks and cleavages; permeability moderately slow; gradual and smooth boundary.

ACh2   60-142 cm   Very dark grey (10YR 3/1) with black (10YR 2/1) shading; clay; strong angular blocky structure; very few mustard size lime nodules effervescing slightly with HCl; very firm and tough when moist, very sticky and plastic when wet, and very hard and compact when dry; permeability slow; clear and sharp boundary.

ACck   142-162 cm   Dark greyish brown (10YR 4/2) clay; many to common lime nodules of different sizes smaller than nut size, giving strong effervescence with HCl; very firm and compact when moist, very sticky when wet and very hard when dry; permeability slow; gradual boundary.

Cck   162-183 cm   Brown (10YR 4/3) with yellowish shading; gravelly clay loam; massive, common lime nodules of various irregular sizes, vigorous effervescence with HCl; firm when moist, sticky when wet and brittle when dry; permeability moderately slow.

CHROMIC VERTISOL

India

Horizon	Depth cm	pH		Cation exchange me %										CaCO$_3$ %
		H$_2$O 1 : 2.5	KCl	CEC	TEB	% BS	Ca	Mg	K	Na	Al	H		
Ap	0—5	7.70	6.5	63.62	58.80		55.5	7.12						0.70
Ah	5—35	7.65	6.5	66.40	61.37		54.5	9.02						0.80
ACh1	35—60	7.70	6.5	65.58	61.94		53.0	9.97						1.24
ACh2	60—142	7.75	6.5	67.22	60.61		52.0	13.17						2.57
ACck	142—162	7.75	6.65	60.66	55.10		38.0	9.50						19.87
Cck	162—183	7.90	6.75	60.94	57.19		37.0	9.50						16.64

Horizon	Sol. salts	Organic matter				Particle size analysis %						Flocc. index	Water-holding capacity	Mois-ture equiv-alent	Avail-able P$_2$O$_5$ lb/acre	Avail-able K$_2$O lb/acre
		% C	% N	C/N	% OM	Stones	Coarse sand	Fine sand	Silt	Clay	Texture					
Ap					0.62		2.27	22.53	20.40	54.80	Clay		87.52	44.11	36.7	400
Ah					0.55		0.49	22.31	22.08	55.12	Clay		82.13	40.70	7.0	280
ACh1					0.55		0.11	25.09	19.20	55.60	Clay		85.04	42.75	5.2	220
ACh2					0.53		0.10	23.50	24.40	52.00	Clay/silty clay		84.40	44.84	1.7	220
ACck					0.18		3.03	32.17	21.60	43.20	Clay		70.82	38.49	3.5	200
Cck					0.18		0.25	32.87	23.76	43.12	Clay/silty clay		71.12	38.06	1.7	180

PELLIC VERTISOL **Vp**

Deep black soil	India
FAO, 1965	p. 80-82
Location	South of Sirpur, Yeotmal district, Maharashtra state, 20° 30'N, 78° 30'E
Altitude	About 275 m
Physiography	Nearly level plain in gently undulating plateau
Drainage	Somewhat poorly drained
Parent material	Basalt
Vegetation	Few dry deciduous trees; mainly under sorghum and cotton
Climate	4.3, hot semitropical, subhumid

Profile description

Ap   **0-2.5 cm**   Very dark grey (10YR 3/1) dry, with very dark brown (10YR 2/2) shading when wet; clay; thin crust and mulch over the Ah horizon; granular to buckshot; loose and pulverescent when dry, friable when moist and sticky when wet; very fine lime nodules, giving slight effervescence with HCl; permeability moderately rapid; clear and smooth boundary.

Ah   **2.5-23 cm**   Very dark grey (10YR 3/1) moist, with slight shading of dark brown colour; clay; cloddy and coarse columnar; shrinks along fissures 5 mm to 7 mm wide, with vertical axis slightly greater than the horizontal; very hard when dry, very firm when moist and very sticky when wet; many very small lime nodules unevenly distributed throughout the horizon, giving slight effervescence with HCl; permeability moderately slow; plentiful fibrous roots; diffused boundary.

ACh1   **23-69 cm**   Very dark grey (10YR 3/1) moist, with black (10YR 2/1) shading; clay; strong angular blocky, with large angular blocky and large angular cleavages; very few fine lime nodules scattered in pockets, giving slight effervescence with HCl; very firm and tough when moist, very sticky and plastic when wet and very hard when dry; few roots in isolated places; permeability slow; gradual boundary.

ACh2   **69-91 cm**   Dark greyish (10YR 4/2) moist, with shading of yellowish brown colour; clay; coarse angular blocky; many lime nodules evenly mixed with peds, giving strong effervescence with HCl, lime nodules increase in number and size and are evenly distributed in the lower part of the horizon; very firm when moist, very sticky when wet and very hard when dry; permeability slow; clear, sharp boundary.

Cck1   **91-132 cm**   Dark yellowish brown (10YR 4/4) moist, with marked yellowish shading; clay loam, evenly mixed with products of primary weathering; coarse and massive; friable when moist; slightly sticky when wet and brittle when dry; common lime nodules, products of *in situ* weathering, giving strong and vigorous effervescence with HCl; permeability moderately rapid.

Cck2   **132+ cm**   The transition of the colour is more prominent; yellowish colour predominates; shrinkage gives the appearance of laminar foliation and peds are small cubes, with compact inner core and partly decomposed outer surface with brown (10YR 5/3) secondary deposits. The cleavages are fine to very fine along both vertical and horizontal axes. The entire ped face is evenly stuffed with lime concretion and secondary lime deposits.

PELLIC VERTISOL

India

Horizon	Depth cm	pH H₂O 1:2.5	pH KCl	CEC	TEB	% BS	Ca	Mg	K	Na	Al	H	CaCO₃ %
						Cation exchange me %							
Ap	0—2.5	7.9	6.7	70.11	67.84		57.0	5.70					1.33
Ah	2.5—23	7.85	6.60	71.82	67.84		59.0	3.32					1.55
ACh1	23—69	7.80	6.60	69.62	65.64		56.0	7.60					2.21
ACh2	69—91	7.80	6.65	68.41	61.32		51.5	6.65					6.81
Cck1	91—132	7.9	6.85	60.29	45.79		36.0	8.07					8.32

Horizon	Sol. salts E.C.	% C	% N	C/N	% OM	Stones	Coarse sand	Fine sand	Silt	Clay	Texture	Flocc. index	Water-holding capacity %	Moisture equivalent %	Available P₂O₅ lb/acre	Available K₂O lb/acre
		Organic matter				Particle size analysis %										
Ap	<0.2				0.76		1.55	21.25	24.56	52.64			89.71	42.92	15.8	360
Ah	<0.2				0.58		0.60	29.00	18.40	52.00			82.62	41.40	12.3	240
ACh1	<0.2				0.58		0.32	35.68	14.00	50.00			84.18	43.54	3.5	200
ACh2	<0.2				0.58		1.72	28.68	20.00	49.60			80.85	42.10	5.2	200
Cck1	<0.2				0.15		29.00	35.00	19.68	16.32			50.20	23.63	1.7	180

HAPLIC XEROSOL   Xh

Haplic Xerosol or Haplic Yermosol	Pakistan
Syal, 1969	Bhalwal series, p. 106 and 164
Location	About 8 km west of Sargodha, 32° 5′N, 72° 30′E
Altitude	About 200 m
Physiography	Nearly level, old river terrace
Parent material	Calcareous, silty, mixed alluvium
Vegetation	Originally scrub savanna; now under irrigated general cropping
Climate	4.2, monsoon subtropical, semiarid

Profile description

Ap   0-15 cm   Brown to dark brown (10YR 4/3) moist and pale brown (10YR 6/3) dry; silty clay loam approaching silt loam; massive; slightly sticky, slightly plastic, friable moist, hard dry; many vesicular and interstitial pores; moderately calcareous; common to many fibrous roots; clear smooth boundary; pH 8.2.

Bw1   15-35 cm   Brown to dark brown (10YR 4/3) moist and brown (10YR 5/3) dry; silty clay loam; very weak coarse subangular blocky; slightly sticky, slightly plastic, firm moist, hard dry; thin patchy cutans; few tubular pores; moderately calcareous; few fibrous and common fine roots; clear smooth boundary; pH 8.2.

Bw2   35-97 cm   Brown to dark brown (10YR 4/3) moist and brown (10YR 5/3) dry; silty clay loam; weak coarse subangular blocky; slightly sticky, slightly plastic, firm moist, hard dry; medium continuous cutans; many fine tubular pores; strongly calcareous; many crotovines; common fine roots; clear smooth boundary; pH 8.3.

BCck   97-137 cm   Brown to dark brown (10YR 4/3) moist and brown (10YR 5/3) dry; silt loam; very weak coarse subangular blocky; sticky, plastic, firm moist, hard dry; thin patchy cutans; few fine interstitial pores; common fine and medium kankers, strongly calcareous; few fine and fibrous roots; diffuse boundary; pH 8.3.

Cck   137-152 cm   Brown to dark brown (10YR 4/3) moist and brown (10YR 5/3) dry; heavy silt loam; massive; slightly sticky, slightly plastic, friable moist, hard dry; no pores; many medium lime specks, strongly calcareous; no roots; pH 8.2.

HAPLIC XEROSOL
Pakistan

Horizon	Depth cm	pH		Cation exchange me%										CaCO₃ %
		H₂O	KCl	CEC	TEB	% BS	Ca	Mg	K	Na	Al	H	
Ap	0—15	7.9											2.0
Bw1	15—35	7.9											2.0
Bw2	35—97	8.0											2.0
BCck	97—137	8.0											9.0
Cck	137—152	7.9											15.0

Horizon	Sol. salts	Organic matter				Particle size analysis %					Flocc. index
	E.C.	% C	% N	C/N	% OM	Stones	Sand U.S.	Silt U.S.	Clay	Texture	
Ap	0.65	0.93	0.08	9			19	48	30		
Bw1	0.50	0.47	0.07	7			19	42	45		
Bw2	0.50	0.40	0.07	6			15	50	35		
BCck	0.92	0.31	0.036	8			11	52	37		
Cck	0.99	0.24	0.036	7							

HAPLIC YERMOSOL Yh

Typic Camborthid	Pakistan
Akram, 1968	p. 161 and 170
Location	About 12 km northeast of Jhang Saddar, 31° 20′N, 72° 25′E
Altitude	About 200 m
Physiography	Nearly level flood plain
Drainage	Well drained
Parent material	Calcareous, mixed alluvium
Vegetation	Under irrigated general cropping
Climate	3.2, hot subtropical desert

Profile description

Ap **0-15 cm** Dark greyish brown (10YR 4/2) moist and light brownish grey (10YR 6/2) dry; loam; massive; slightly sticky, slightly plastic, friable moist, hard dry; few medium, fine and common very fine interstitial pores; moderately calcareous; few medium and fine roots; clear smooth boundary; pH 8.4.

Bw1 **15-46 cm** Brown to dark brown (10YR 4/3) moist and pale brown (10YR 6/3) dry; silt loam; weak coarse and medium subangular blocky; slightly sticky, slightly plastic, friable moist, slightly hard dry; few medium, common fine and many very fine tubular pores; thin nearly continuous cutans in pores; moderately calcareous; common worm casts; few medium and common fine roots; clear smooth boundary; pH 8.2.

Bw2 **46-69 cm** Brown to dark brown (10YR 4/3) moist and pale brown (10YR 6/3) dry; few fine faint yellowish brown (10YR 5/6) mottles; silt loam; weak coarse subangular blocky; slightly sticky, slightly plastic, friable moist, slightly hard dry; few fine and many very fine tubular pores; moderately calcareous; few worm casts; few fine and many very fine roots; clear smooth boundary; pH 8.2.

BC **69-80 cm** Brown to dark brown (10YR 4/3) moist and pale brown (10YR 6/3) dry; few fine faint yellowish brown (10YR 5/6) mottles; silt loam; very weak coarse subangular blocky with few laminations of very fine sandy loam; slightly sticky, slightly plastic, friable moist, slightly hard dry; few fine and many very fine tubular pores; moderately calcareous; few coarse sand pockets; few worm casts; few fine and many very fine roots; clear wavy boundary; pH 8.2.

C **80-94 cm** Brown to dark brown (7.5YR 4/2) moist; few fine distinct yellowish brown (10YR 5/6) and few fine faint dark yellowish brown (10YR 4/4) mottles; silt loam (approaching silty clay loam); massive; sticky, plastic, firm moist, hard dry; few fine and many very fine tubular pores; few very fine kankers; few laminations moderately calcareous; few worm casts; few fine roots; clear wavy boundary; pH 8.2.

2C **94-137 cm** Brown (10YR 5/3) moist; few medium distinct yellowish brown (10YR 5/6) and few fine faint olive brown (2.5Y 4/4) mottles; very fine sandy loam; massive and weak thin platy; slightly sticky, slightly plastic, very friable moist, slightly hard dry; common fine and very fine tubular pores; few sand specks; few very fine kankers; moderately calcareous; few fine roots; abrupt smooth boundary; pH 8.2.

3C **137-140 cm** Brown to dark brown (7.5YR 4/2) moist; few medium faint dark yellowish brown (10YR 4/4) and few fine distinct yellowish brown (10YR 5/8) mottles; silty clay; massive; sticky, plastic, firm moist, very hard dry; few fine and common very fine tubular pores; few sand specks; few fine kankers; moderately calcareous; pH 8.4.

HAPLIC YERMOSOL
Pakistan

Horizon	Depth cm	pH H₂O paste	KCl	CEC	TEB	% BS	Ca	Mg	K	Na	Al	H	CaCO₃ %
						Cation exchange me %							
Ap	0—15	8.1											
Bw1	15—46	8.4											
Bw2	46—69	8.2											
BC	69—80	7.9											
C	80—94	7.9											
2C	94—137	7.9											

Horizon	Sol. salts E.C.	% C	% N	C/N	% OM	Sand	Silt U.S.	Clay	Texture	Flocc. index
		Organic matter				Particle size analysis %				
Ap	1.1					47	35	18	Loam	
Bw1	0.66					7	67	26	Silt loam	
Bw2	1.3					2	71	27	Silt loam/silty clay loam	
BC	1.8					4	69	27	Silt loam/silty clay loam	
C	2.2					3	66	31	Silty clay loam	
2C	2.4					9	62	29	Silty clay loam	

CALCIC YERMOSOL   Yk

Typic Calciorthid	Iran
Van de Weg, 1967	p. 28-29 and analytical data tables
Location	One km north of Darband Sofla, approx. 34°N, 46°E
Altitude	About 600 m
Physiography	Nearly level to very gently sloping piedmont plain
Drainage	Well drained
Parent material	Mixed, calcareous alluvium
Vegetation	Originally Mesopotamian steppe; now under wheat, dryland farming.
Climate	6.8, subtropical semiarid Mediterranean

Profile description

Ap	**0-15 cm**	Yellowish brown (10YR 5/4 dry, 4/2 moist) clay loam; cloddy, breaking into granular structure; hard; some pores and roots; smooth gradual boundary.
Bwk1	**15-35 cm**	Brown (7.5YR 5/4) clay loam; fine weak angular blocky structure; hard; a few lime mycelia and spots; a few roots; smooth gradual boundary.
Bwk2	**35-70 cm**	Brown (7.5YR 4/4) silty clay; moderate coarse angular blocky structure; many lime mycelia and lime points; a few roots; compact horizon; smooth gradual boundary.
BCk	**70-140 cm**	Brown (7.5YR 4/4) silty clay; strong coarse angular blocky structure; many mycelia and lime points; compact horizon; some thin clay cutans.

NOTE: Colours given are for moist soils. All horizons are calcareous.

CALCIC YERMOSOL

Iran

Horizon	Depth cm	pH H₂O paste	KCl	Cation exchange me % CEC	TEB	% BS	Ca	Mg	K	Na	Al	N	CaCO₃ %
Ap	0—15	7.5		50.0						0.45			16.65
Bwk1	15—35	7.6		46.0						0.53			37.70
Bwk2	35—70	7.6		48.0						0.51			23.23
BCk	70—140	7.7		46.0						0.61			29.78

Horizon	Sol. salts E.C.	Organic matter % C	% N	C/N	% OM	Particle size analysis % Stones	Sand	Silt U.S.	Clay	Texture	Flocc. index	CaSO₄
Ap	48	1.21					31.0	38.6	30.4	Clay loam		10.59
Bwk1	48	0.32					39.6	36.0	24.4	Loam		11.73
Bwk2	49	0.51					31.0	36.4	32.6	Clay loam		11.76
BCk	50	0.30					37.0	38.4	24.1	Loam		11.75

Horizon	Soluble cations and anions Ca	Mg	Na	K	Sum cations	CO₃	HCO₃	Cl	SO₄	Sum anions
Ap	6.6	1.9	1.05	—	9.05	0	3.0	2.0	4.6	9.6
Bwk1	5.0	0.5	1.1	—	6.6	0	2.0	2.0	3.0	7.0
Bwk2	4.5	0.5	1.1	—	6.1	0	2.0	2.5	1.5	6.0
BCk	2.0	3.0	1.4	—	6.4	0	1.0	4.0	1.6	6.6

CALCIC YERMOSOL   Yk

Saline gypsiferous desert soil   Kuwait

Ergun, 1969	Profile 35, p. 57
Location	Northwest of Sadda, approx. 28°N, 48°E
Altitude	About 90 m
Physiography	Rolling to undulating
Drainage	Imperfect to poor
Parent material	Gypsiferous and calcareous sandy clay loam
Vegetation	Mediterranean semidesert shrub
Climate	3.2, hot subtropical desert

Profile description

Ah   0-11 cm   Pale brown (10YR 6/3) to brown (10YR 5/3) moist; sandy loam to sandy clay loam; massive; friable; strongly calcareous.

Bwck   11-34 cm   Light yellowish brown to brownish yellow (10YR 6/5) to yellowish brown (10YR 5/5) moist; weak fine granular; sandy clay loam; $CaCO_3$ concentration; strongly calcareous.

BCck   34-70 cm   Light brownish grey to light yellowish brown (2.5Y 6/3) to light olive brown (2.5Y 5/4) moist; sandy clay loam; more $CaCO_3$ accumulation than horizon above.

Ccky   70-100 cm   Light grey (2.5Y 7/2) moist; sandy clay loam; gypsum and $CaCO_3$ particles; moderately calcareous.

CALCIC YERMOSOL

Kuwait

Horizon	Depth cm	pH		Cation exchange me %									CaCO₃ %
		H₂O	KCl	CEC	TEB	% BS	Ca	Mg	K	Na	Al	H	
Ah	0—11												
Bwck	11—34												
BCck	34—70												
Ccky	70—100												

Horizon	Sol. salts.	Organic matter				Particle size analysis %				Flocc. index
		% C	% N	C/N	% OM	Sand	Silt	Clay	Texture	
Ah						68.0	12	20	Sandy loam/sandy clay loam	
Bwck						69.0	12	19	Sandy loam	
BCck						56.0	20	24	Sandy clay loam	
Ccky						57.0	9	34	Sandy clay loam	

GYPSIC YERMOSOL   Yy

Typic Gypsiorthid	Iraq
F.H. Altaie, 1968	p. 119 and 120
Location	About 50 km north of Baghdad
Altitude	About 250 m
Physiography	Nearly level, high Tigris terrace
Parent material	Gravelly gypsiferous old alluvium
Vegetation	Extensive grazing: *Artemisia scoparia*, *Plantago ovata*, *Stipa capenais*, *Achillea santolina L.* and others
Climate	Mean annual temperature 23°C, mean annual rainfall 150 mm

---

Profile description

Ah   0-6   cm   Dark brown (7.5YR 4/4) moist; loam; weak medium platy structure; very friable moist; calcareous; little gravel; low organic matter, very many fine roots; clear smooth boundary.

Cy1   6-20   cm   Brown (7.5YR 5/3) moist; mixed gypsiferous materials; granular; friable moist; calcareous; low organic matter; no roots; gradual smooth boundary.

Cy2   20-50   cm   Dark brown (7.5YR 4/3) moist; mixed gypsiferous materials; friable moist; granular; calcareous; no roots; diffuse smooth boundary.

Cy3   50-80   cm   Brown (7.5YR 5/3) moist; mixed gypsiferous materials; friable moist; granular; slightly calcareous; little gravel; diffuse smooth boundary.

Cy4   80-110 cm   Brown (7.5YR 5/3) needle-like mixed gypsiferous materials; very low in lime; about 10% gravel; diffuse smooth boundary.

Cy5   110-170 cm   Brown (7.5YR 5/3) moist; needle-like mixed gypsiferous materials; very low in lime; about 20% gravel; diffuse smooth boundary.

Cy6   170-500 cm   Brown, mixed gypsiferous soils; about 70% gravel; thin bands of sand.

GYPSIC YERMOSOL
Iraq

Horizon	Depth cm	pH H₂O	pH KCl	CEC Soil	CEC Clay	% BS	Ca	Mg	K	Na	Al	Gypsum	CaCO₃ %
						Cation exchange me %							
Ah	0—6	7.6		13.0	62				0.6	0.1		1.1	23.2
Cy1	6—20	7.7		6.8	36				0.2	0.1		60.0	5.3
Cy2	20—50	7.7		6.2	41				0.2	0.3		48.2	2.0
Cy3	50—80	7.7		5.8	29				0.1	0.3		56.7	1.2
Cy4	80—110	7.6		7.4	30				0.1	0.4		55.1	1.5
Cy5	110—170	7.8		8.2	36				0.2	0.8		48.8	5.2

Horizon	Sol. salts	% C	% N	C/N	% OM	Stones	Sand	Silt	Clay	E.C. mmhos/cm sat. ext.	P ppm
		Organic matter									
Ah					0,94		30	49	21	2.9	4.4
Cy1					0,43		32	49	19	3.3	3.9
Cy2					0,25		39	46	15	4.0	3.9
Cy3					0,11		48	32	20	3.5	3.9
Cy4							44	31	25	3.5	3.9
Cy5							46	31	23	3.8	tr.

Horizon	Ca⁺⁺	Mg⁺⁺	Na⁺⁺	Cl⁻	SO₄⁻⁻	HCO₂⁻	Fe₂O₃ %
	Soluble anions and cations meq/l						
Ah	32.0	1.2	1.5	1.8	29.2	1.3	
Cy1	34.0	1.2	1.5	1.8	31.8	1.0	0.05
Cy2	32.8	1.6	4.4	6.4	31.8	0.8	0.04
Cy3	33.6	2.0	4.1	6.4	33.0	0.8	0.05
Cy4	32.0	2.0	4.9	6.4	32.2	0.6	
Cy5	31.6	1.6	7.1	6.0	32.0	1.5	0.05

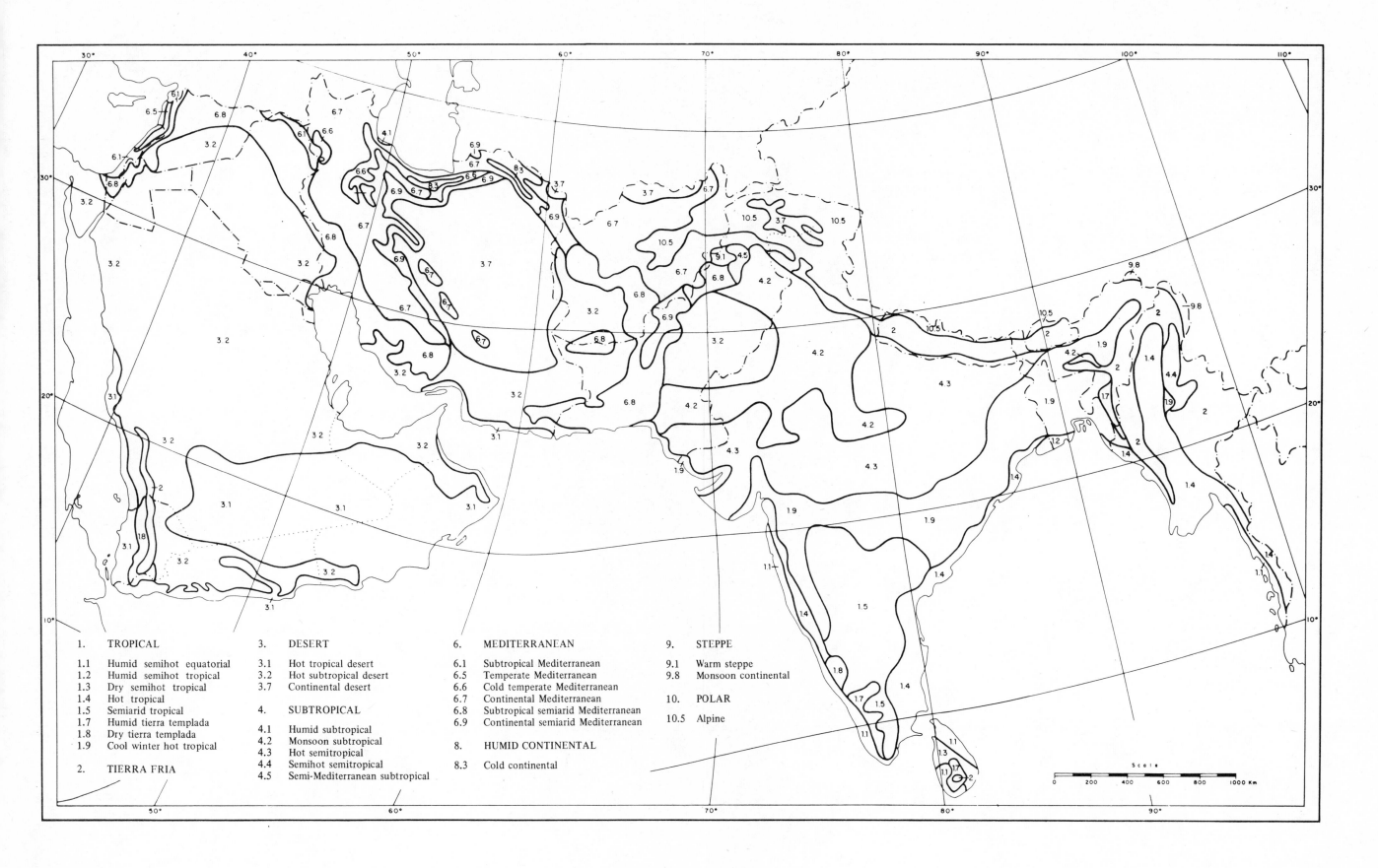

1.   TROPICAL

1.1   Humid semihot equatorial
1.2   Humid semihot tropical
1.3   Dry semihot tropical
1.4   Hot tropical
1.5   Semiarid tropical
1.7   Humid tierra templada
1.8   Dry tierra templada
1.9   Cool winter hot tropical

2.   TIERRA FRIA

3.   DESERT

3.1   Hot tropical desert
3.2   Hot subtropical desert
3.7   Continental desert

4.   SUBTROPICAL

4.1   Humid subtropical
4.2   Monsoon subtropical
4.3   Hot semitropical
4.4   Semihot semitropical
4.5   Semi-Mediterranean subtropical

6.   MEDITERRANEAN

6.1   Subtropical Mediterranean
6.5   Temperate Mediterranean
6.6   Cold temperate Mediterranean
6.7   Continental Mediterranean
6.8   Subtropical semiarid Mediterranean
6.9   Continental semiarid Mediterranean

8.   HUMID CONTINENTAL

8.3   Cold continental

9.   STEPPE

9.1   Warm steppe
9.8   Monsoon continental

10.   POLAR

10.5   Alpine

Scale

0   200   400   600   800   1000 Km

1. CLIMATES

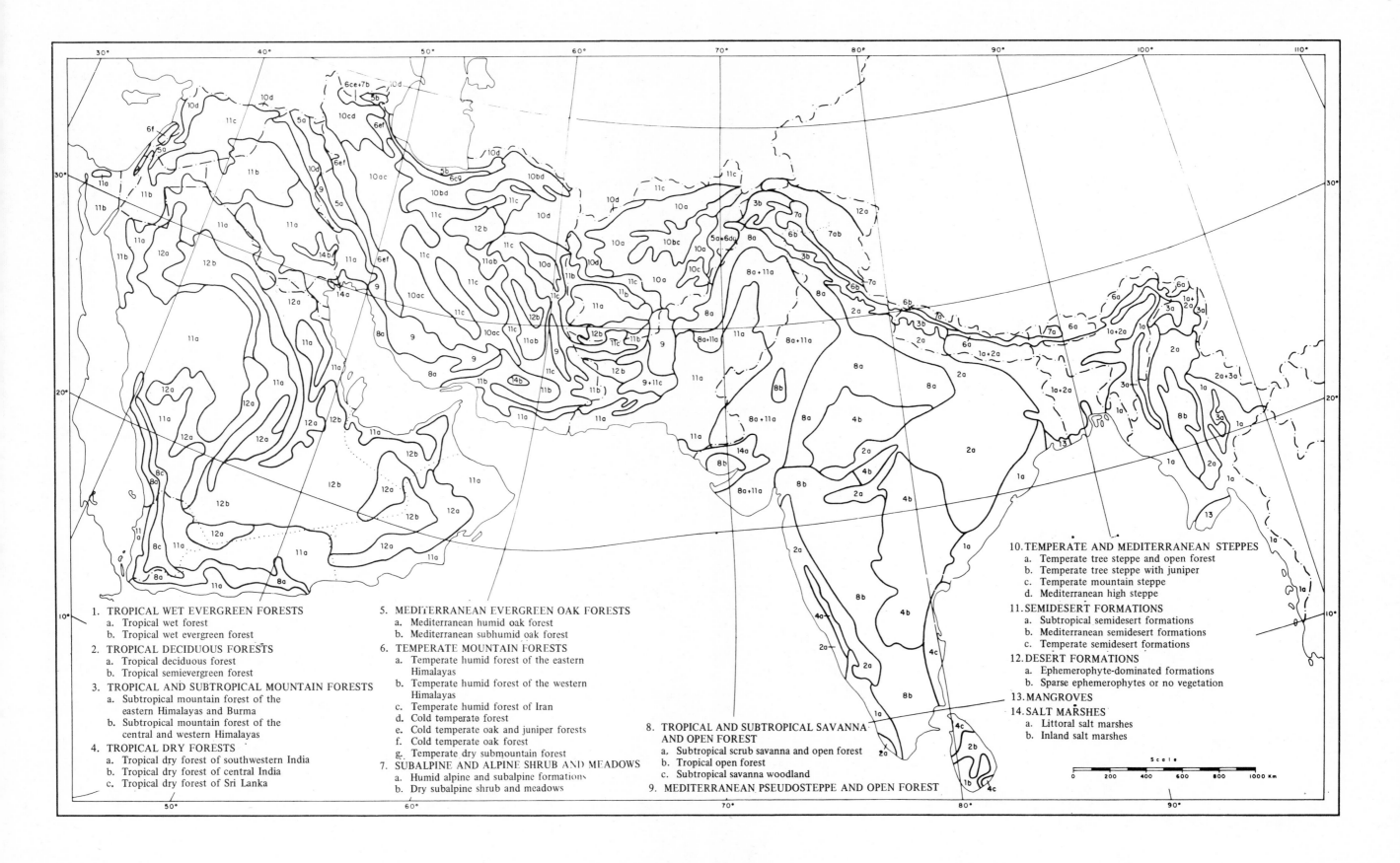

1. TROPICAL WET EVERGREEN FORESTS
   a. Tropical wet forest
   b. Tropical wet evergreen forest
2. TROPICAL DECIDUOUS FORESTS
   a. Tropical deciduous forest
   b. Tropical semievergreen forest
3. TROPICAL AND SUBTROPICAL MOUNTAIN FORESTS
   a. Subtropical mountain forest of the
      eastern Himalayas and Burma
   b. Subtropical mountain forest of the
      central and western Himalayas
4. TROPICAL DRY FORESTS
   a. Tropical dry forest of southwestern India
   b. Tropical dry forest of central India
   c. Tropical dry forest of Sri Lanka

5. MEDITERRANEAN EVERGREEN OAK FORESTS
   a. Mediterranean humid oak forest
   b. Mediterranean subhumid oak forest
6. TEMPERATE MOUNTAIN FORESTS
   a. Temperate humid forest of the eastern
      Himalayas
   b. Temperate humid forest of the western
      Himalayas
   c. Temperate humid forest of Iran
   d. Cold temperate forest
   e. Cold temperate oak and juniper forests
   f. Cold temperate oak forest
   g. Temperate dry submountain forest
7. SUBALPINE AND ALPINE SHRUB AND MEADOWS
   a. Humid alpine and subalpine formations
   b. Dry subalpine shrub and meadows

8. TROPICAL AND SUBTROPICAL SAVANNA
   AND OPEN FOREST
   a. Subtropical scrub savanna and open forest
   b. Tropical open forest
   c. Subtropical savanna woodland
9. MEDITERRANEAN PSEUDOSTEPPE AND OPEN FOREST

10. TEMPERATE AND MEDITERRANEAN STEPPES
    a. Temperate tree steppe and open forest
    b. Temperate tree steppe with juniper
    c. Temperate mountain steppe
    d. Mediterranean high steppe
11. SEMIDESERT FORMATIONS
    a. Subtropical semidesert formations
    b. Mediterranean semidesert formations
    c. Temperate semidesert formations
12. DESERT FORMATIONS
    a. Ephemerophyte-dominated formations
    b. Sparse ephemerophytes or no vegetation
13. MANGROVES
14. SALT MARSHES
    a. Littoral salt marshes
    b. Inland salt marshes

Scale
0   200   400   600   800   1000 Km

2. VEGETATION

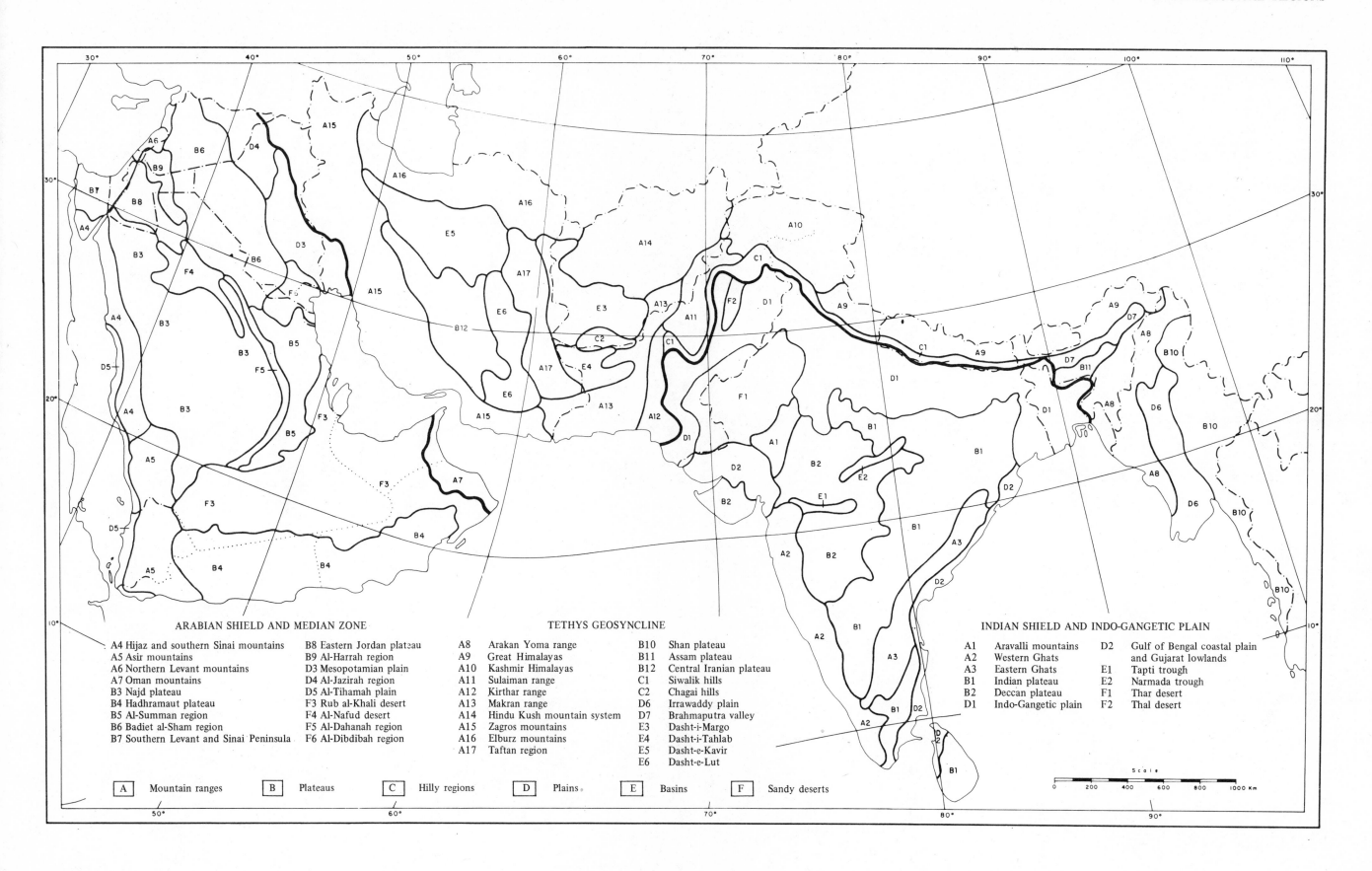

ARABIAN SHIELD AND MEDIAN ZONE

A4 Hijaz and southern Sinai mountains
A5 Asir mountains
A6 Northern Levant mountains
A7 Oman mountains
B3 Najd plateau
B4 Hadhramaut plateau
B5 Al-Summan region
B6 Badiet al-Sham region
B7 Southern Levant and Sinai Peninsula

B8 Eastern Jordan plateau
B9 Al-Harrah region
D3 Mesopotamian plain
D4 Al-Jazirah region
D5 Al-Tihamah plain
F3 Rub al-Khali desert
F4 Al-Nafud desert
F5 Al-Dahanah region
F6 Al-Dibdibah region

TETHYS GEOSYNCLINE

A8 Arakan Yoma range
A9 Great Himalayas
A10 Kashmir Himalayas
A11 Sulaiman range
A12 Kirthar range
A13 Makran range
A14 Hindu Kush mountain system
A15 Zagros mountains
A16 Elburz mountains
A17 Taftan region

B10 Shan plateau
B11 Assam plateau
B12 Central Iranian plateau
C1 Siwalik hills
C2 Chagai hills
D6 Irrawaddy plain
D7 Brahmaputra valley
E3 Dasht-i-Margo
E4 Dasht-i-Tahlab
E5 Dasht-e-Kavir
E6 Dasht-e-Lut

INDIAN SHIELD AND INDO-GANGETIC PLAIN

A1 Aravalli mountains
A2 Western Ghats
A3 Eastern Ghats
B1 Indian plateau
B2 Deccan plateau
D1 Indo-Gangetic plain

D2 Gulf of Bengal coastal plain
   and Gujarat lowlands
E1 Tapti trough
E2 Narmada trough
F1 Thar desert
F2 Thal desert

A Mountain ranges   B Plateaus   C Hilly regions   D Plains   E Basins   F Sandy deserts

Scale
0   200   400   600   800   1000 Km

3. GEOMORPHOLOGY

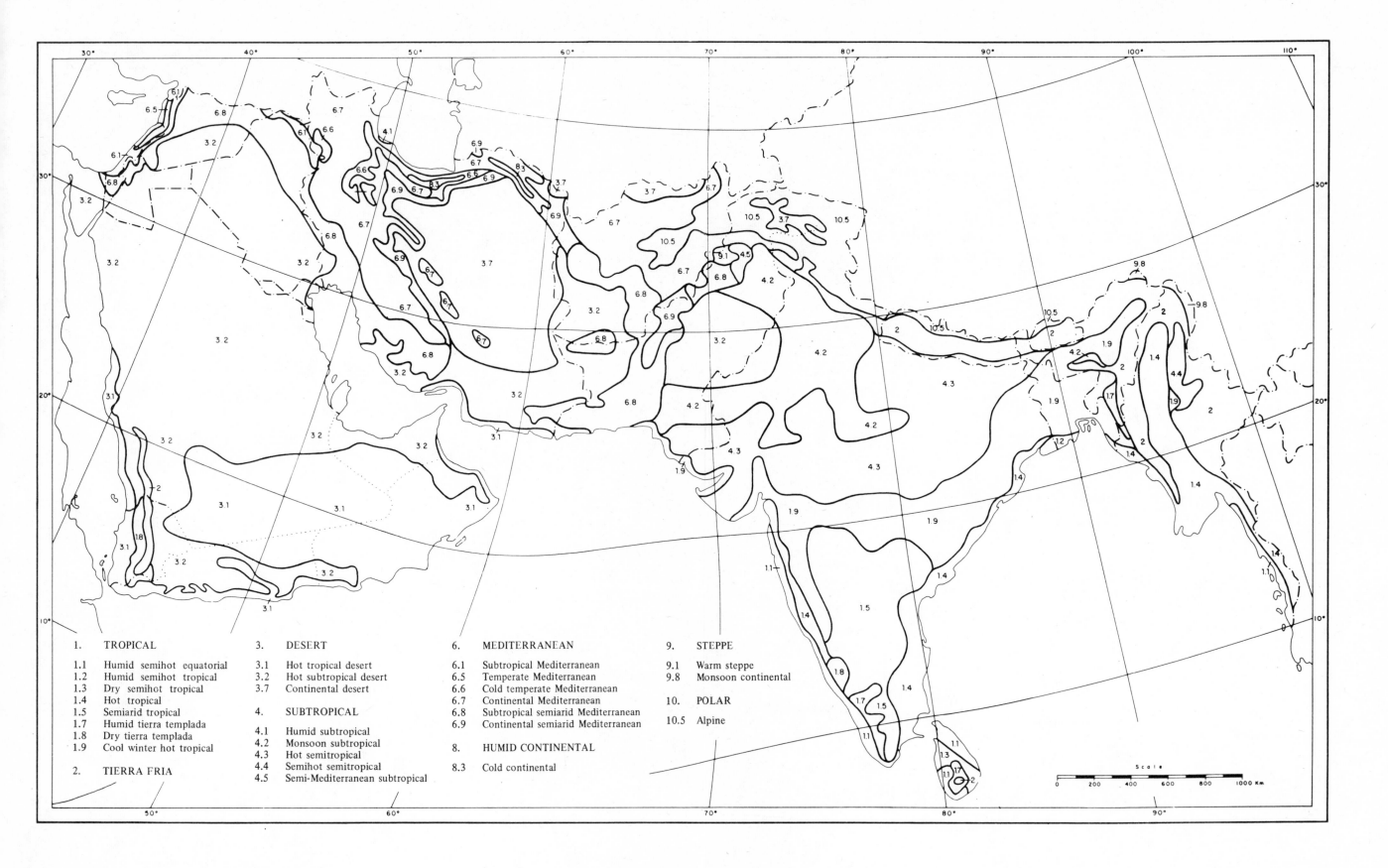

1.   TROPICAL

1.1   Humid semihot equatorial
1.2   Humid semihot tropical
1.3   Dry semihot tropical
1.4   Hot tropical
1.5   Semiarid tropical
1.7   Humid tierra templada
1.8   Dry tierra templada
1.9   Cool winter hot tropical

2.   TIERRA FRIA

3.   DESERT

3.1   Hot tropical desert
3.2   Hot subtropical desert
3.7   Continental desert

4.   SUBTROPICAL

4.1   Humid subtropical
4.2   Monsoon subtropical
4.3   Hot semitropical
4.4   Semihot semitropical
4.5   Semi-Mediterranean subtropical

6.   MEDITERRANEAN

6.1   Subtropical Mediterranean
6.5   Temperate Mediterranean
6.6   Cold temperate Mediterranean
6.7   Continental Mediterranean
6.8   Subtropical semiarid Mediterranean
6.9   Continental semiarid Mediterranean

8.   HUMID CONTINENTAL

8.3   Cold continental

9.   STEPPE

9.1   Warm steppe
9.8   Monsoon continental

10.   POLAR

10.5 Alpine

Scale

0   200   400   600   800   1000 Km

1. CLIMATES

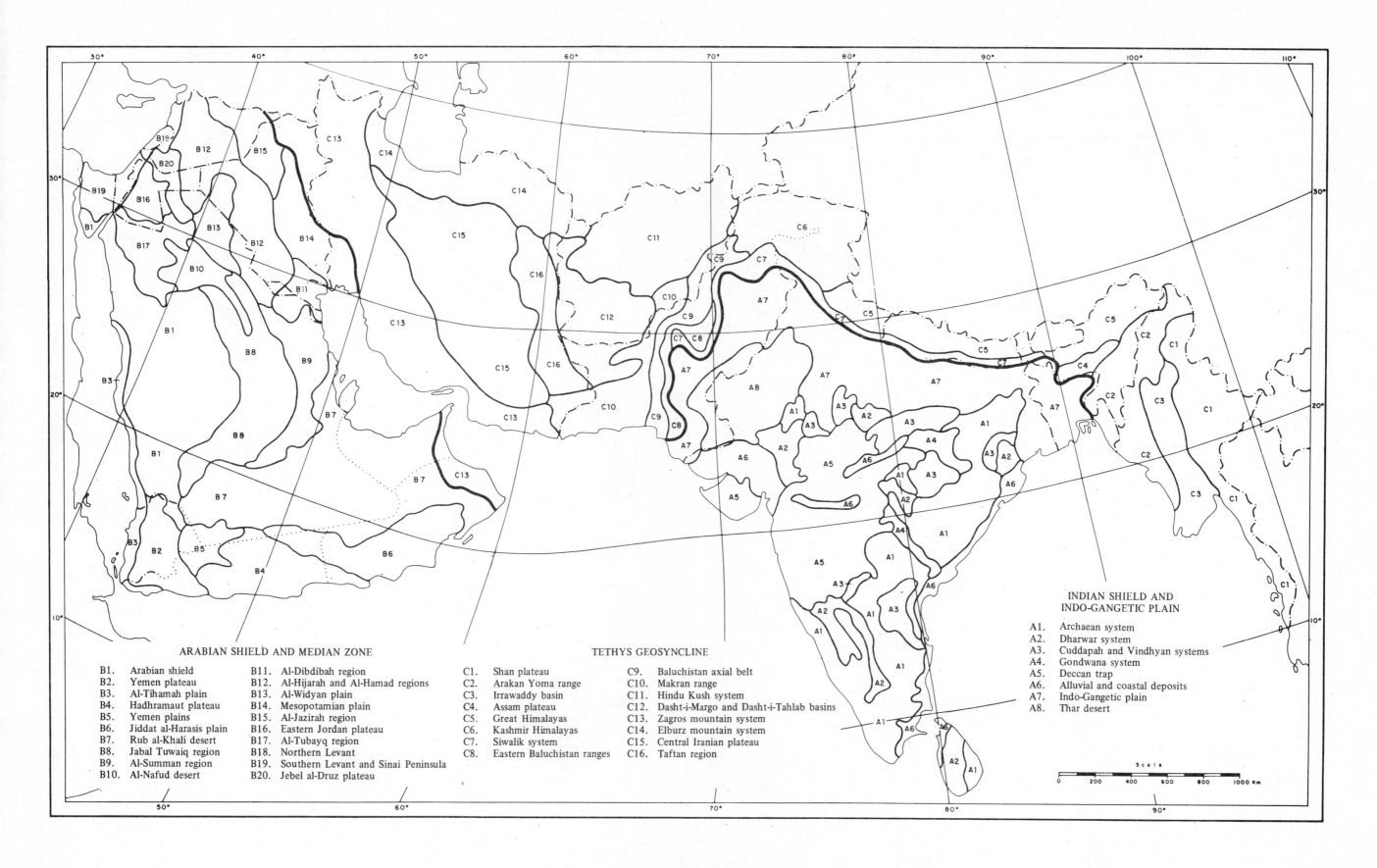

ARABIAN SHIELD AND MEDIAN ZONE

B1.	Arabian shield	B11.	Al-Dibdibah region
B2.	Yemen plateau	B12.	Al-Hijarah and Al-Hamad regions
B3.	Al-Tihamah plain	B13.	Al-Widyan plain
B4.	Hadhramaut plateau	B14.	Mesopotamian plain
B5.	Yemen plains	B15.	Al-Jazirah region
B6.	Jiddat al-Harasis plain	B16.	Eastern Jordan plateau
B7.	Rub al-Khali desert	B17.	Al-Tubayq region
B8.	Jabal Tuwaiq region	B18.	Northern Levant
B9.	Al-Summan region	B19.	Southern Levant and Sinai Peninsula
B10.	Al-Nafud desert	B20.	Jebel al-Druz plateau

TETHYS GEOSYNCLINE

C1.	Shan plateau	C9.	Baluchistan axial belt
C2.	Arakan Yoma range	C10.	Makran range
C3.	Irrawaddy basin	C11.	Hindu Kush system
C4.	Assam plateau	C12.	Dasht-i-Margo and Dasht-i-Tahlab basins
C5.	Great Himalayas	C13.	Zagros mountain system
C6.	Kashmir Himalayas	C14.	Elburz mountain system
C7.	Siwalik system	C15.	Central Iranian plateau
C8.	Eastern Baluchistan ranges	C16.	Taftan region

INDIAN SHIELD AND
INDO-GANGETIC PLAIN

A1.	Archaean system
A2.	Dharwar system
A3.	Cuddapah and Vindhyan systems
A4.	Gondwana system
A5.	Deccan trap
A6.	Alluvial and coastal deposits
A7.	Indo-Gangetic plain
A8.	Thar desert

Scale

0   200   400   600   800   1000 Km

4. GEOLOGY

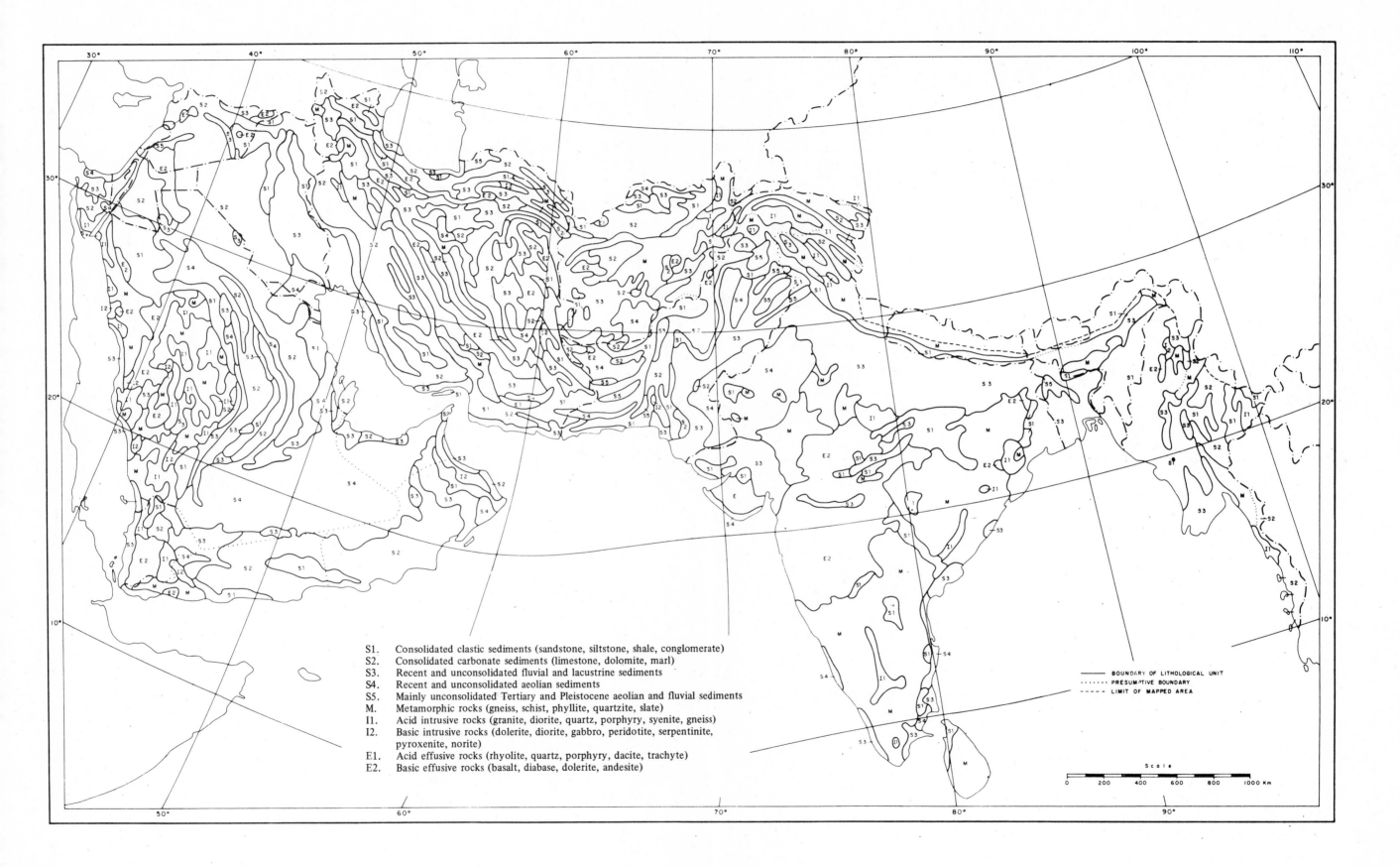

S1. Consolidated clastic sediments (sandstone, siltstone, shale, conglomerate)
S2. Consolidated carbonate sediments (limestone, dolomite, marl)
S3. Recent and unconsolidated fluvial and lacustrine sediments
S4. Recent and unconsolidated aeolian sediments
S5. Mainly unconsolidated Tertiary and Pleistocene aeolian and fluvial sediments
M. Metamorphic rocks (gneiss, schist, phyllite, quartzite, slate)
I1. Acid intrusive rocks (granite, diorite, quartz, porphyry, syenite, gneiss)
I2. Basic intrusive rocks (dolerite, diorite, gabbro, peridotite, serpentinite, pyroxenite, norite)
E1. Acid effusive rocks (rhyolite, quartz, porphyry, dacite, trachyte)
E2. Basic effusive rocks (basalt, diabase, dolerite, andesite)

———— BOUNDARY OF LITHOLOGICAL UNIT
.... PRESUMPTIVE BOUNDARY
– – – – LIMIT OF MAPPED AREA

Scale
0   200   400   600   800   1000 Km

5. LITHOLOGY

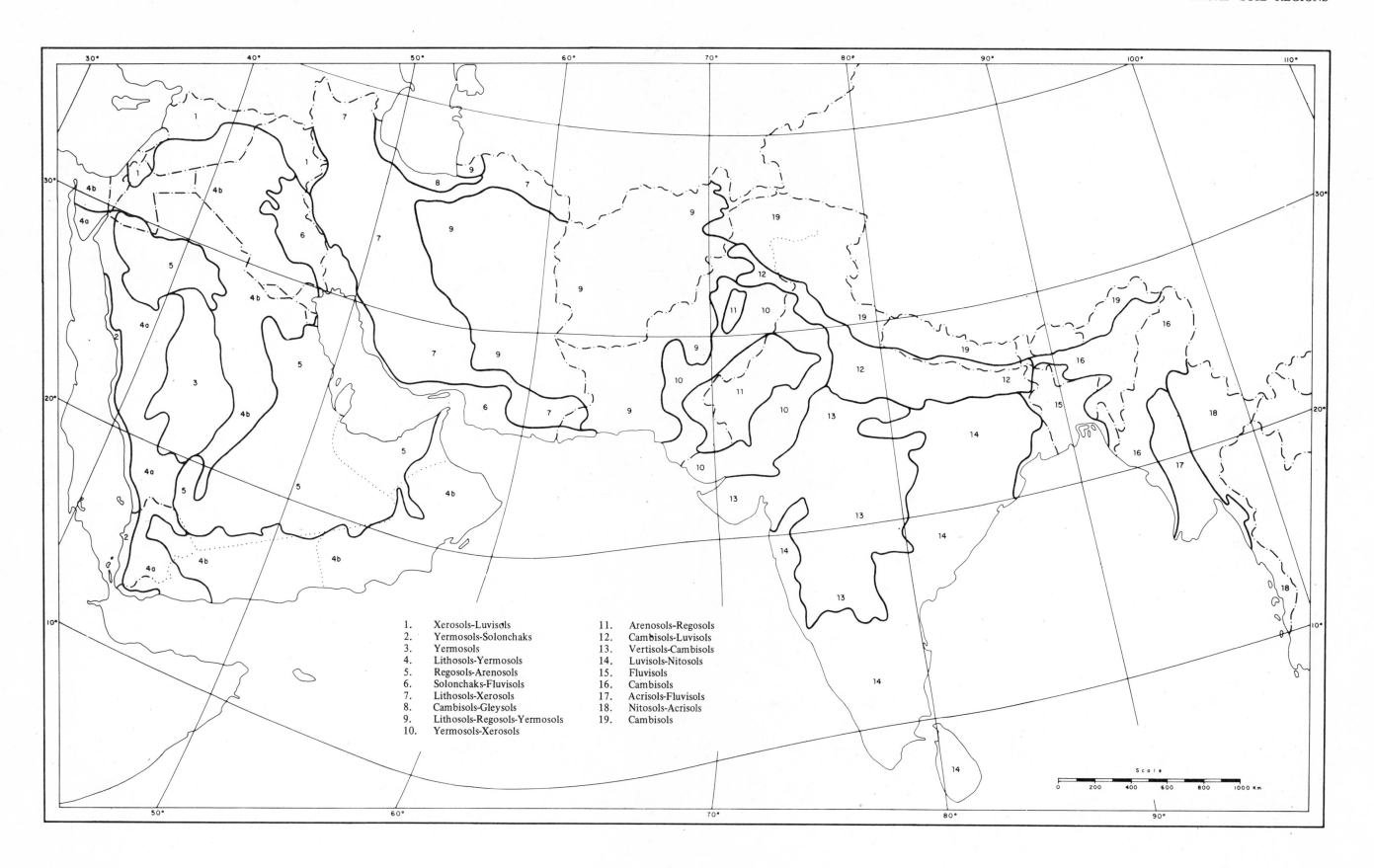

1. Xerosols-Luvisols
2. Yermosols-Solonchaks
3. Yermosols
4. Lithosols-Yermosols
5. Regosols-Arenosols
6. Solonchaks-Fluvisols
7. Lithosols-Xerosols
8. Cambisols-Gleysols
9. Lithosols-Regosols-Yermosols
10. Yermosols-Xerosols
11. Arenosols-Regosols
12. Cambisols-Luvisols
13. Vertisols-Cambisols
14. Luvisols-Nitosols
15. Fluvisols
16. Cambisols
17. Acrisols-Fluvisols
18. Nitosols-Acrisols
19. Cambisols

Scale
0   200   400   600   800   1000 Km

6. SOILS